THE GREAT EXHIBITION
of the Industry of all Nations,
Opened by Her Majesty Queen Victoria
MAY 1ST 1851.

VICTORIAN DESIGNS for NEEDLEPOINT

by Phyllis Kluger

Holt, Rinehart and Winston
New York

We would like to thank the following for the use of their photographs and artwork: Picture collection of The New York Public Library: pp.ii, viii, 20; Chicago Convention and Tourism Bureau, Inc.: p. 22; The Catalogue of The Great Exhibition of 1851: pp. 24, 56, 77; Detail of Rookery lobby, Chicago Historical Society: p. 26; David Holbrook: pp. 30, 68; Petit Courrier des Dames: p. 32; Edmund V. Gillon, Jr.: pp. 34, 60, 80; L. Scott: p. 38; The British Museum: p. 39; Mr. E. Richard Levy, Office of the City Representative, Fairmount Park Commission of the City of Philadelphia: p.44; Dover Publications: pp.42, 50, 73; Joseph P. Ziolo: p.46; Victoria and Albert Museum: p. 48; Cooper-Hewitt Museum, the Smithsonian Institution's National Museum of Design, Gift of Cowtan and Tout, 1935-23-30: p. 51; The Illuminated Book of Needlepoint: pp. 58, 59; Philip Wiseman: p. 62; The Preservation Society of Newport County: p. 64; Adele Earnest, Stony Point Folk Art Gallery: p. 66; Museum of the City of New York: p. 76.

Published simultaneously in Canada by
Holt, Rinehart and Winston of Canada, Limited.

Library of Congress Cataloging in Publication Data
Kluger, Phyllis.
Victorian designs for needlepoint.

1. Canvas embroidery—Patterns. 2. Canvas
embroidery, Victorian. I. Title.
TT778.C3K6   746.4'4   78-2396

ISBN Hardbound: 0-03-020436-4
ISBN Paperback: 0-03-044946-4

First Edition

Designer: Sheila Lynch

Printed in the United States of America

2 4 6 8 10 9 7 5 3 1

For my Mother and Father

Many people make contributions toward the publication of a single book. Among those I would like to thank for their efforts are Ellyn Polshek, my editor, Sheila Lynch, designer and researcher, and David Holbrook, a gifted and patient photographer. Joan Arbeiter was, as ever, extremely helpful to me. Very special thanks have to be given to my husband, Richard, for many reasons.

Contents

Twenty-three color plates follow page 54.

Interior, Crystal Palace, Great Exhibition of 1851, London

Preface

The British and American peoples now seem to be carrying on a love affair with the Victorian era and the age of feckless indulgence that began just before the Queen's accession in 1837 and ended with the onset of the Great War in 1914. This is perhaps more revealing of Britain and America's present problems than the genuine glories of the past.

We may speculate on the reasons for this phenomenon. More than escapism, certainly, seems involved. A major part of the attraction, no doubt, is that the Victorian and Edwardian world, with all its excesses and gaucherie, was a time of bursting energy and boundless hope. Each new machine and its instant harnessing gave massive evidence of progress in human affairs. Indeed "progress" was the byword of the age, the faith of the century, and one could see the signs of it—the proliferation of manufactured goods, the spread of material comforts, the expansion of the British Empire, and the transcontinental trek of the Americans—all around. A purpose and a pattern, under God's apparent blessing, seemed to guide the swelling wealth of the Anglo-Saxons as they rose to world dominion. Today, a different world faces us, progress and wealth are no longer simple equivalents, the relative power of Britain and America has fallen sharply, and hence a yearning for that radiant yesteryear-that-never-quite-was serves us as a kind of balm.

The Victorians were the pioneer beneficiaries (as well as the victims) of the arrival of the industrial age. For the first time, man had the means to fashion the raw materials of the earth into goods that were within the purchasing power of great numbers of people. Poverty, to be sure, was the continuing lot of the masses, and industrial exploitation produced cruelties no less grinding than those of the pre-industrial age, but technology and capitalism combined to bring life's advantages—or some of them, at any rate—to a dramatically widening middle class. The world was no longer arranged solely to accommodate the whims of the wafer-thin upper crust. And with this sudden arousal of aspiration among multitudes came a blossoming of the decorative arts on a scale the world had never seen before.

Few objects could be purchased that were not embellished in some way, from the handles of scissors encrusted with lilies of the valley to the parlor stove adorned with flying cherubs holding aloft elaborate scrollwork.

If, today, "Victorian" has become a nearly generic description of an artistic style that one associates with ornamentation, with previously unimagined combinations of historic styles, this is no reason to exclude it from the realm of legitimate artistic examination. Quite the contrary. For here was an age so caught up in its endeavors, so proud of its growing success, that it could hardly wait to show off by garnishing itself from top to bottom. The unwritten aesthetic of the age was that if an object contained a surface that could be fancied up, then it should be so embellished. The principle applied to the possessions of not just the rich but the enterprising middle class. And not just to luxury goods but to everyday wares. And not just in mansions but in cottages from Manchester to the Channel.

It was not a time of innovation in art; it was, rather, an age of decoration, of celebration of man's suddenly burgeoning possibilities, and nowhere on earth were those possibilities more apparent than in Britain and America. Political and economic gains among the masses—the broadening of the franchise in Great Britain, monetary reforms and land and work for the asking in the United States—accompanied technological strides, and soon a social revolution no less vast than the industrial one was unfolding. People in all stations of life had a new pride in themselves and showed it in their fondness for embellishing whatever they could afford to own.

This book of Victorian designs examines this remarkable impulse by focusing on decorative examples from the fields of industrial design, architecture, domestic furnishings, and personal ornaments and creating from them needlepointed tributes to the age of progress.

VICTORIAN DESIGNS
for
NEEDLEPOINT

How to Use This Book

<u>Victorian Designs for Needlepoint</u> is a collection of thirty-two patterns for needlepoint canvas, all of which can be used in a variety of ways. Suggestions for the use of each design have been included along with the width and height of each piece of finished needlework, as a guide to enable you to plan your own work (in all measurements, width precedes height). There is no reason, though, why you cannot ignore my suggestions completely and use any design in any way you like. In fact, a little imagination on your part—say, using a center pattern of one design with borders from another—can turn any design into a work that is uniquely your own. If I have used red, green, and white in a pattern, there is no reason why you should not use yellow, orange, and rust for your own design if those shades are more in keeping with the color scheme in your home or in your imagination. If I used the basketweave stitch for a background and you prefer the interlocking Gobelin stitch, go to it!

Needlepoint is a general term for a kind of embroidery worked on loosely woven canvas. If there are many threads to the square inch of canvas and, therefore, a great number of stitches to the square inch of embroidery, the work is referred to as petitpoint. Conversely, if there are just a few threads to the inch and, consequently, a small number of stitches, the resulting embroidery is called grospoint, or quickpoint. The only difference is in the scale of the canvas and the stitches.

Both kinds of embroidery and most needlepoint are done on canvas with a blunt needle and lengths of yarn. All needlepoint canvas is "sized," which means that it is heavily starched to retain its cross-hatched shape. As a result of handling, the canvas gradually loses its stiffness and becomes increasingly soft. As the canvas has softened, you must take pains not to pull the yarn through it too tightly or the canvas will be permanently distorted and no amount of blocking will ever straighten it out.

2

Canvas

Canvas comes in various widths and sizes and is usually sold by the fraction of a yard. There is petitpoint canvas that contains twenty-four threads, or open spaces called mesh, to the inch and grospoint canvas, mostly for rugs or large cushions, that holds just four threads or mesh to the inch. There is a difference, too, between a kind of double-thread canvas, usually called Penelope, and single-thread, or mono, canvas. Penelope canvas generally measures ten mesh to the inch, but because each mesh is made up of two warp threads and two woof threads, a single basketweave or continental stitch covers an intersection of four threads. It is customarily used when one wants to stitch petitpoint and grospoint on the same piece of canvas, as each intersection of the double threads can be worked separately for the smaller stitches. Since none of the designs in this collection was stitched on Penelope, the word canvas as used here means mono canvas only, and the number used to describe it (#14, #10, etc.) refers to the number of vertical and horizontal threads per inch of canvas.

There is little point in trying to save money on canvas. In my experience, cheaper canvas is of lesser quality than the more expensive kind. Blocking a piece of work (see page 8) entails pulling the canvas with great force, and cheaper material has been known to break under the pressure. Don't buy canvas that contains knots or irregularities or you may wind up with uneven stitches, which can ruin your work.

Needles

Blunt-tipped needles with long, narrow eyes—called tapestry needles—are used for needlepoint. They come in various sizes, sometimes several sizes to a package. I use a #18 needle for work that employs two or three strands of Persian yarn on #10 to #14 canvas. For other canvas I use a smaller or larger needle accordingly. Threading the needle often takes a bit of practice, since yarn, unlike sewing thread, is not moistened and twisted to make a point, but is folded once around the needle, held close to the fold, and, thus doubled, pushed through the long eye. For some needlepointers, the technique is best learned in a demonstration, and salespeople are usually happy to show you just how to do it.

Yarn

Although it is possible to use different kinds of yarn, from silk to linen, when doing needlepoint, the kind of woolen yarn called Persian is easiest for the beginner to use and comes in a wide range of shades. It is also possible to purchase small quantities for experimental purposes. Persian is a 3-strand yarn and can be split so that only two strands are used when working smaller-meshed canvas—#14, #16, or #18, for example—or used with a full three strands on #12, #10, or #8. It may even be doubled or tripled for an extremely large-mesh canvas. In general, yarn should be thick enough to cover the canvas threads so that none of them show through the stitches, but not so thick as to distort the meshes or canvas threads.

I prefer to use #13 or #14 canvas for most projects. It is small enough to keep designs from coarsening, but large enough to prevent eyestrain. Most of the samples in this collection were worked on #13 or #14 canvas.

Graphs

A graph that conveys the color and placement of each stitch has been included for every pattern in the book. Most of the needlework patterns were executed in the basketweave and continental stitches. In general, remember that the continental stitch is best for outlining designs and for working small areas. For filling in large areas and backgrounds, I prefer the basketweave stitch because it distorts the canvas least.

As a rule, in designs that employ only basketweave or continental stitches, each square of a graph represents one basketweave or continental stitch. Where I have used other stitches, the Stitch Dictionary following this section indicates how those stitches are done, and the text with each design explains how and where to use them. Where designs use a combination of Bargello and basketweave stitches, I have tried to ensure that the graphs indicate this clearly. You will notice that every ten stitches on the graphs have been ruled off with a heavy line. This facilitates stitch-counting and can aid in estimating the relative size of any design.

If marking off the canvas into squares that conform to the graphs seems to be helpful, remember to use a waterproof pen. There are pens sold in art-needlework stores that are supposed to be waterproof, but it is best to be skeptical about these pens and test them first. Make a few lines with the pen on a piece of scrap fabric. Saturate the cloth with water and allow it to dry. If the ink has bled at all, don't use that pen! It is foolish to try to save a little time at the start of your work only to ruin the result. If a truly waterproof pen can't be found, there are a couple of alternatives. You can use a tiny brush and oil paint thinned with turpentine to make your lines. When dry, this paint is waterproof. Or you can thread a needle with colored sewing thread and run it through the canvas with basting stitches both horizontally and vertically every ten rows. The canvas is then marked to conform to the graph. After the pattern is established on the canvas with yarn, the colored threads can be pulled out with no danger of future damage to your work. Of course, if you are a confident needlepointer and don't mind counting stitches, you can plunge ahead on an unblemished canvas. For me, the challenge of working on a clean canvas is worth the risk that I'll make a mistake (and I make them fairly frequently).

One way to make the graphs easier to follow is to color the printed squares with crayons or pens. Should you want to keep the pages unmarked, the book can be held open with a light paperweight, a pair of scissors, for example (something heavy will break the binding), and a large rubber band can be slipped over the cover and intervening pages to mark your place on the pattern chart. As you progress, the band can be rolled along the edges of the cover to follow the pattern. Another way to indicate your place is to attach a piece of paper to the page with a paper clip. As you "read" the chart, you can slide the paper down the page until the pattern section is completed. In both cases, no permanent damage is done to the book and the graphs can be followed relatively easily.

All of the graphs have been executed so that no less than one repeat of the design pattern has been provided. In other words, if a pattern is bilaterally symmetrical, at least half of it has been graphed and the missing section is just a mirror image of its counterpart. Thus, it is often possible to turn the book upside down and work the other side from the same pattern. Occasionally, there is a pattern in which a quarter of the whole is charted. In that case, the book should be given a 90° turn in order to follow the chart. In all cases, the written instructions that accompany each pattern are intended to provide additional help. When in doubt, compare the chart with the color photograph of the completed design.

Planning Your Project

Let's use one pattern as a specific example—the unexpected Gothic Water Tower in the midst of Chicago's deluxe shopping area (see page 22). A look at the color plate reveals the finished work, but you will find only a little more than a quarter of the design on the graph. By studying both the chart and the photograph, though, you can see that the design is the same on both sides and the bottom half is exactly the same as the top half. That means that since the upper left side of the design has been graphed, the upper right side has to look exactly like it, but in reverse, a mirror image. On turning the book upside down, you will discover that if the graph is read thus, the lower right half has also been graphed and that the left side should follow the pattern of the right one but also in reverse.

Let us suppose, though, that you do not own a footstool, as in the example, nor do you want to buy one. Instead, you want to make a 16-inch-square pillow using the same design. The instructions indicate that #13 canvas was used for the work and that the footstool measures 15″ by 11½″. Because the scale of the design seems appropriate for a 16″ by 16″ pillow, you decide to stay with #13 canvas, just as in the example. In #13 canvas there are, of course, 13 threads or mesh to the inch (there is occasionally some variation in canvas and it doesn't always measure out exactly, so it is better to err on the side of generosity when planning). You count the squares on the graph and find a total of 60 stitches from the left-side edge up to and including the center stitch (which means that there will be 59 stitches on the upper right side that has not been graphed) and 78 stitches from the top of the design to the center stitch (and, therefore, 77 stitches in the bottom section of the design that is not shown on the graph). The whole design then measures 78 + 77, or 155, stitches from top to bottom by 60 + 59, or 119, stitches from left to right. By dividing 13 (the number of threads to the inch in #13 canvas) into 155 and 13 into 119, the figures can be rounded off to 12 and 9 respectively. You then know that the finished design will measure approximately 12 inches in length by 9 inches in width. But since a 16″ by 16″ pillow is desired, a background of at least 3½ inches on either side of the design and 2 inches above and below has to be added in order to create a pillow surface 16 inches square. The arithmetic becomes automatic with practice, I promise!

Needlepoint canvas does tend to shrink a bit when blocked. To allow for this, it is best to provide at least an extra inch when stitching, and even more when the design is a particularly large one. The process of blocking requires that a margin of at least 2 inches of unworked canvas be left around each piece of needlepoint. The purchase of only one-half yard of #13 canvas would allow only 18 inches to work with, and that's not enough for the pillow. A person who likes to allow for mistakes should buy three-quarters of a yard of canvas, or 27 inches. That provides lots of room and even extra canvas to make something else.

Before embarking on a project, you must bind the cut edges of the canvas with masking tape so that they do not ravel, and then, if you like, run a basting stitch through the canvas every ten threads. After the center of the canvas is found, you can sense the approximate surface the design will cover and can finally go to work with needle and yarn.

I start my canvases by knotting the end of the first strand of yarn and pulling the needle through the canvas from front to back about 1½″ away from the place where I intend to put my first stitch. I position it so that it is immediately in the path of the first several stitches I will make. As these stitches are worked, they will secure the 1½″ of yarn that lie on the back of the canvas between the knot itself and the start of the first stitch. After the stitches are completed and the end of the yarn is securely incorporated into the needlework, the knot on the front of the canvas can be cut off (carefully, of course, so that none of the work around the knot is damaged). To end off a strand of yarn, I pull the needle through the work on the wrong side of the canvas for about 1½″ and cut off any little pieces remaining. Little tails hanging from the wrong side of your work just look sloppy. I find it easiest to outline my work first in continental stitches and fill in with basketweave after the design has been defined.

These processes become second nature to every experienced needlepointer, and the necessity for counting every ten rows of canvas threads disappears with practice. No matter how much experience you have, however, you will still find it necessary to do some thinking before purchasing materials because planning a canvas is an integral part of the creative process itself. Since canvas is manufactured in so many sizes, you must decide what scale you want the finished design to be. Altough the proportions of any design in this collection will remain the same no matter what the size of the canvas, the scale will, of course, be radically different if you use #18 canvas or #5 rug canvas. Because both the canvas size and the finished size of the needlepointed sample are given in this collection, you can visualize the scale of any design and can then decide if that is suitable for your needs and, if not, make the necessary changes. A design can be repeated twice or three times or indefinitely until the desired size is obtained, and it can be scaled up or down by using a larger or smaller size canvas. It is a matter of perspective, need, and suitability. Obviously, a handbag carried to a black-tie event would seem a mite peculiar if it were made of rug yarn on #5 canvas. On the other hand, the same yarn and canvas could very well be used for a large bag brought to the beach.

What to Do with Your Completed Needlepoint

Just what is it that needlepoint can be used for? While suggestions for the use of each design have been included in the text, here is a basic concept that should stimulate your own imagination: Worked needlepoint canvas is nothing more than a rather heavy fabric and can be used wherever a thick, stiff fabric would work. Clearly, it serves well as upholstery, around containers of all sorts (from buckets to luggage), and as a covering for inanimate objects (from pianos to floors). The only place needlepoint does not work very well is in covering the moving parts of the human body. Stiff canvas has little "give" to it and functions best around the less mobile human parts. A needlepoint jacket might wind up a disaster around the elbows, say, and I would hate to bend my knees in a pair of needlepoint jeans. But a belt or a vest works beautifully. A needlepointed mini-skirt I made a decade ago worked just fine, but I would hesitate to make the longer skirts of this era. Historically, needlepoint was used to make bed curtains and valences, and there is no reason why it could not be so used today. I was once advised by a workman in the Metropolitan Museum of Art that the best way to treat a wall was to upholster it and thereby assure that it would last for decades. (Of course it might take you that long to finish the job.) If you happen to own a historic dwelling and are reasonably sure it will remain in your family for the next several generations, then go ahead and needlepoint your wall-covering. It will more than likely be the first one on your block.

Many needlepointers prefer to have their work finished professionally. I would agree that most pieces do look better when they are executed by people who are in the business of upholstering chairs, for example, or framing pictures, or making handbags with leather linings. If you are able to afford such treatments, then by all means do so. If not, or if you are a do-it-yourself devotee, you can use the advice I have given in the Instructions for Finishing Projects section beginning on page 82. All of the projects shown here were executed in their entirety by the author, even the upholstery.

Blocking

Undoubtedly the most tiresome chore in working needlepoint is blocking it. For years I was too cowardly to try it myself, but eventually I reached a point where it became a necessity. Blocking your work is necessary to stabilize the shape and to straighten it out so that a finished item can be made from it. After a piece is worked, no matter how carefully, a certain amount of distortion and softening of the canvas occurs. The neat little right-angled mesh boxes of the original canvas become irregular diamond-shaped blobs. The object of blocking work is to bring it back to its crisp, right-angled shape.

The materials needed are few, but the assembly process takes a bit of time and energy. You'll need some rustproof pins or tacks, a sheet of brown paper, a flat surface that can take the holes you're about to put into it, and a couple of right angles. I have used a sheet of plywood as a blocking board but prefer homosote, a very thick cardboard-like substance sold at building-supply stores. Although pushpins work in homosote, they often leave rusty scars on the canvas, so I prefer to use the T-pins sold at hobby shops for children's model-building.

The first thing to do is to wet the canvas. I use my plant mister for this, spraying the canvas until it is good and wet but somewhat short of dripping. This should cause the masking tape at the edge of the canvas to curl up and start to come unglued, but pay no attention. After all, you are supposed to have at least 2″ of unworked canvas around the edges. Try hard, though, not to pull out the canvas threads as you block. Next, place the canvas right side up on a clean surface. This is where the sheet of brown paper is needed to cover the plywood or homosote. Now comes the physical part. Put several pins along one edge of the canvas every inch or so, checking with a ruler to make sure the edge is straight. Then take the right angles (metal carpenter's tools are best because they are unbreakable and incorporate rulers along the sides) and fit them into the corners to ensure that each corner measures 90°. This is sometimes a difficult job, which involves much tugging and pulling because just as one corner measures 90°, two others may be somewhat short of it, or wider than a right angle and so adjustments have to be made on all the edges. This can sometimes take quite a while and involves a great deal of physical effort. (Don't be afraid to pull on the canvas, because it is meant to take this kind of stress. This is also why you were advised earlier to buy the best canvas available.) The process will be a kind of pulling-and-pinning, pulling-and-pinning. Eventually, all four angles will measure out perfectly, at which point pins should be inserted in the canvas every half-inch around the edge. The canvas should be left pinned to the board until it is thoroughly dry, usually overnight. The next day, take a look at the work, pull out the pins, and check the angles again. If the middle of the canvas is taut and flat and all four corners measure 90°, you're home free. If, on the other hand, there is a large wrinkle in the middle of the canvas and all four corners (or only one or two) measure more or less than 90°, it's a do-over. But it will work on the second or even the third try, and you'll finally feel triumphant.

All of the foregoing is aimed at starting you on your way toward creating things that you will be proud to own and even prouder to have made yourself. The craft of needlepoint can be stimulating or relaxing, and perhaps even both simultaneously; but it is, above all, a benign addiction, and once you've started, it may prove almost impossible to stop. I know. I've been addicted for almost twenty years and my head is still full of things I'm eager to do.

Stitch Dictionary

Following are descriptions and step-by-step diagrams of the stitches used in this collection of needlepoint patterns. In all of the numbered stitch illustrations, the odd numbers indicate where the needle comes out of the canvas from back to front, and the even numbers show where the needle goes into the canvas from front to back. The stitches are presented in alphabetical order.

An explanation of the use of "compensation" in needlepoint, a technique for linking differing stitches where there is no room to complete a stitch pattern, follows the stitches on page 18.

BARGELLO STITCH

The Bargello stitch (as it shall be referred to in this book) is a series of long, vertical stitches that cover two or more horizontal threads of the canvas. The long stitches can be arranged in a variety of ways to make

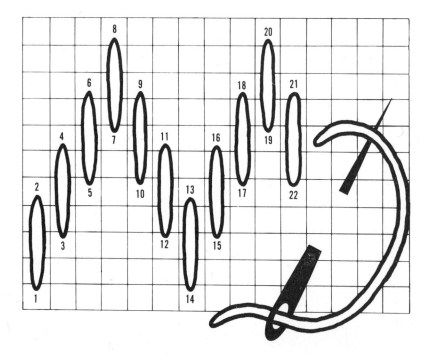

different kinds of stitch patterns. Flamestitch patterns in which the stitches are placed to form a series of peaks and valleys in a manner similar to the arrangement on the evening bag (New Haven Bracket design—Color Plate 12) and mosaic diamond stitch, the beige background of the Chicago Water Tower footstool design (Color Plate 13), are two patterns created with the Bargello stitch.

Bring the needle out from the back of the canvas to the front at square #1; cross over four horizontal threads above and put it back into the canvas at square #2. Bring it out again at #3, back in again at #4, and so on.

BASKETWEAVE STITCH

The basketweave stitch looks very much like the continental or tent stitch on the right side of the work, but on the hidden side it resembles a kind of coarse weaving, hence its name. It is a series of small, diagonal stitches that cover the intersection of one vertical and one horizontal thread of the canvas. Basketweave is worked in diagonal rows in both directions, from top to bottom of the canvas and back again. It can be tricky to learn at first, but a little practice will reinforce the process. Because basketweave does not distort the canvas as badly as the continental stitch, it is the preferred stitch for filling in large areas and backgrounds.

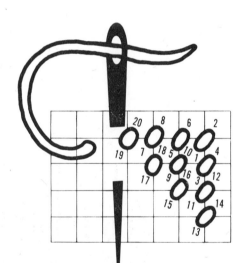

In this stitch, the needle emerges from the back of the canvas to the front at #1 and goes back through the canvas at #2. It comes back out at #3, returns to the back side of the canvas at #4, emerges at #5, returns to the back at #6, etc. Following the numbers, it can be seen that by the time #12 has been finished the third "row" of basketweave work has been accomplished. The first stitch, #1 to #2, became the first row; the second and third stitches, #3 to #4 and #5 to #6, became the second diagonal row; the third diagonal row was completed by the three stitches #7 to #12. The next diagonal row is comprised of the four stitches #13 to #20. Work continues in a similar fashion, with each diagonal row crossing the canvas from upper left to lower right and vice versa.

BRICK STITCH

The brick stitch is a series of Bargello-like stitches that form a brick effect as they work out. The stitch is a good one, particularly for backgrounds, because it goes quite rapidly and is relatively sparing of yarn. As it is used here, the stitch covers four canvas threads (although it can be used to cover only two) and each stitch is separated from the one that follows it by two horizontal canvas threads (or, when the stitch is only half as long, by a single canvas thread).

The stitch can be accomplished most easily by following the numbers. The needle comes out from the canvas at square #1 of the diagram and returns back into the canvas at #2, having covered four horizontal threads in a single stitch. Square #3, where the needle next emerges from the back of the canvas, is one thread over, right next to the first stitch but two threads below #2. The stitch that is created when the needle returns to the back of the canvas at #4 also covers four horizontal threads and lies immediately next to the first stitch but two threads up from it. The row continues in this way, with each stitch two threads higher or lower than the stitch that immediately preceded it.

The second row, which begins at #15 crossing four threads below #14, and all subsequent rows, continue in this "one-stitch-up, one-stitch-down" fashion.

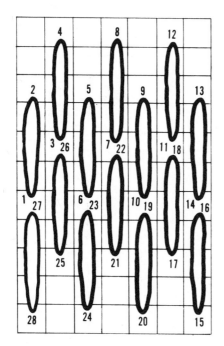

CONTINENTAL STITCH

The continental, or tent, stitch looks just like the basketweave stitch and the half cross stitch, but it is done very differently. The half cross stitch does not have much yarn at the back of the work and is, therefore, less substantial. For making upholstery, pillows, and other objects that will have to take hard wear, the basketweave and continental stitches are preferred. For pictures or other items that will not be subjected to much abrasion, the half cross stitch is fine. The continental and basketweave stitches can be used interchangeably, but the basketweave is more practical for large areas because the continental stitch distorts the canvas rather badly. Continental works best for outlines or very small areas. The numbers on the diagram indicate how the stitches are to be worked on the canvas. This stitch can be worked vertically and horizontally—left and right and up and down—as the diagrams show.

In Figure 1, the continental stitch is shown being worked in a horizontal row from right to left. Figure 2 shows the horizontal second row worked from left to right. Figure 3 illustrates the stitch worked vertically from top to bottom of the canvas, and in Figure 4, a vertical row of continental stitches is worked from bottom to top.

The easiest way for novices to execute the stitch properly is to remember that the object of the continental stitch is to leave more, rather than less, yarn on the back of the canvas. For this reason, the needle, as shown on the diagrams, always goes under two canvas threads and comes back to make the stitch over one thread intersection, no matter what the direction.

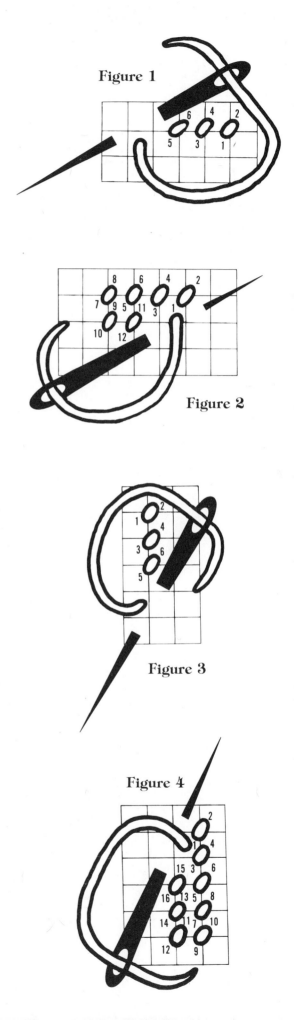

Figure 1

Figure 2

Figure 3

Figure 4

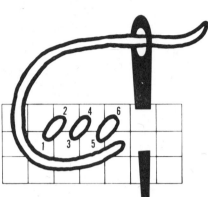

Figure 1

CROSS STITCH

The cross stitch is a crewel stitch that can be done as effectively on needlepoint canvas as on cloth. Because it is necessary to ensure that all of the stitches cross in the same direction, it is easier to do all of the southwest-to-northeast stitches first, as shown in Figure 1 (thus forming the "half cross stitch") and then crossing the stitches in the southeast-to-northwest direction, as shown in Figure 2.

To begin the second row of cross stitches, the needle emerges from the back of the canvas at A and returns to the back of the canvas at B. Continue in the same manner as shown in the instructions for the first row.

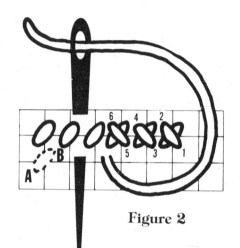

Figure 2

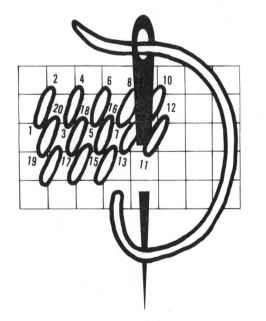

INTERLOCKING GOBELIN STITCH

The interlocking Gobelin stitch is a kind of diagonal Bargello stitch. The stitch as shown on the diagram covers two horizontal canvas threads and one vertical thread so that it becomes a "two-up-and-one-across" mental picture for me. If the yarn is thick enough to conceal the canvas beneath it, you can also stitch over three or even four horizontal threads at once. This stitch gives a smooth, satiny finish to the front of the piece and can be worked in horizontal rows in either direction.

KNOTTED STITCH

The knotted stitch is a two-step process that is worked from right to left. As can be seen from the diagrams, it is a kind of uneven cross stitch. The long arm of the stitch is a "three-up-and-one-across" formula. Figure 1 shows the long arm being stitched (#13 to #14). The second step of the process would be a tiny stitch that covers the intersection of two canvas threads (#15 to #16) to form the "knot." In Figure 2 the small cross is made. It is a tight, secure stitch, difficult to snag, that forms a series of raised, horizontal ridges.

LEVIATHAN STITCH

The Leviathan stitch is really a double cross stitch. The four thicknesses of yarn in the center of the stitch form a rather large bump, and thus a canvas featuring this stitch possesses an attractively tactile surface. In this book, the Leviathan stitch is used as the background for the Lace by Machine design (see page 24), which was derived from a piece of lace. Because lace motifs are connected to each other with threads, I decided that, in this design, the lace threads would be represented by the small stitches shown in black in Figure 2 below. These stitches were executed in white against the blue background in the pattern as seen in Color Plate 20.

After the large double crosses of the Leviathan stitches are completed (see Figure 1), the small stitches for the lace "threads" are worked over them. Either a backstitch or a series of small basting stitches can be used, with all the stitches going in one direction made first and the others filled in on the return trip. The little stitches sometimes have to be almost forced into the canvas because, as can be seen in the diagram, these stitches are placed in canvas meshes that are already occupied by four threads of the large Leviathan-work and thus already very crowded.

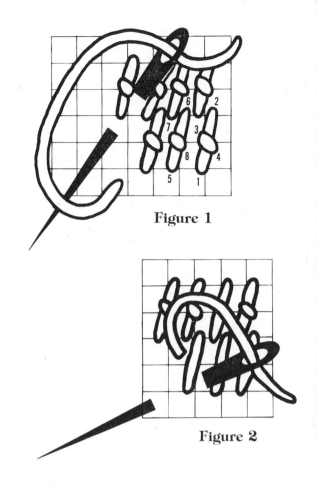

Figure 1

Figure 2

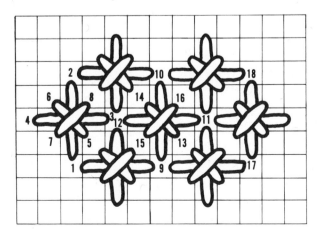

Figure 1

Figure 2

TRUE CROSS STITCH

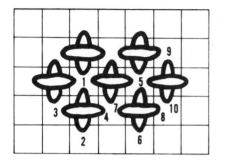

The true cross stitch is a variation of the X-shaped cross stitch. In this arrangement, each of the two elements of the stitch covers two threads, horizontally and vertically. The numbers on the chart indicate how the stitch is to be done, starting from the lower left stitch. Here, too, as with other kinds of cross stitches, care must be taken to ensure that the horizontal yarn always lies atop the vertical one. Because this cross stitch is larger than the X-shaped one, the effect of two strands of yarn lying over each other is more pronounced and a bumpy texture is achieved when the stitch is used over a large area.

WHIPPED SPIDER WEB

The whipped spider web is generally used for accent purposes only. The horizontal and vertical ribs of the web cover six canvas threads, while the diagonal ribs cover four thread intersections. The sequence of stitching the ribs does not matter particularly, but after the ribs are done, the needle should emerge to the front of the canvas through the square next to the center one, as shown in Figure 1. The web is whipped from the center outward and the needle moves clockwise around the ribs, under two and back over one in a kind of backstitch, in crewel-work terms, for this is another instance of needlepoint borrowing from crewel embroidery. In whipping the "web," the needle does not penetrate the canvas at all; the entire motif lies on top of the canvas and is anchored only by the ribs. In executing a web of this size on #13 needlepoint canvas with two strands of Persian yarn in the needle, I found that six rounds of whipping were sufficient to fill out the length of the ribs (see Figure 4).

Figures 1-3 show the yarn covering the first two ribs. As each rib is covered with yarn, the needle is pulled very slightly so that the yarn-covered rib will stand out from the yarn that lies beneath it. When the whipped spider web is completed, there will be no space visible at the center hole.

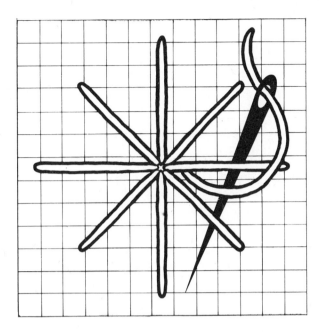

Figure 1

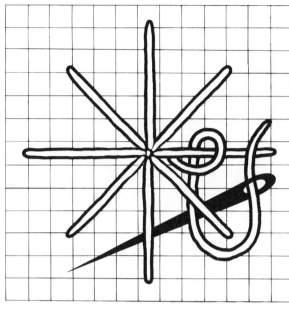

Figure 2

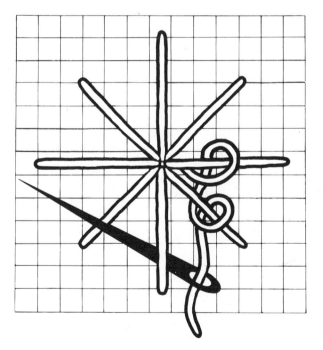

Figure 3

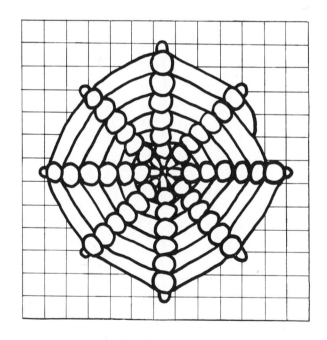

Figure 4

COMPENSATION

Compensation refers to the use of continental or basketweave stitches to make a transition between a patterned stitch that may exist in one area of a piece of work and the continental or basketweave stitches in another area. In this diagram, white Bargello stitches arranged in a brick-stitch pattern are used as a background. Nearby is part of a design that employs black continental stitches. Since the Bargello work must end (because there is no room to continue it on the canvas without interfering with the black-stitched design), there remains a gap between the Bargello stitches and the start of the black basketweave. The gap is bridged by the use of white basketweave stitches to ensure that the black and white areas remain clearly delineated, and that no unstitched canvas is showing.

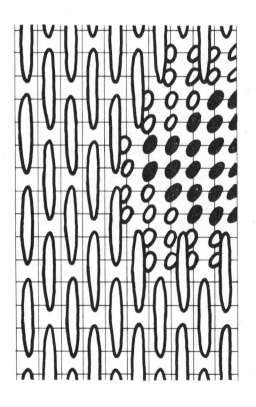

PORTFOLIO
of
DESIGNS

SOUTH KENSINGTON GRILLWORK

(see Color Plate 13)

The South Kensington Museum was built in 1866, the brainchild of Prince Albert, Queen Victoria's consort. He had envisioned the museum as a showplace exhibiting the wonders that had been made possible by the new union of art and science. Now a part of the Victoria and Albert Museum complex, the structure features a pediment that houses a tilework figural composition. The Queen is shown in classical garb, receiving tribute from representations of the Arts and Sciences. Behind the figures in the foreground is an outline of Paxton's Crystal Palace, the glass-walled edifice built for the Great Exhibition of 1851.

Just beyond the pediment is a course of lacy grillwork that served as the source of this pattern, which has been stitched on #14 canvas. The design is a string of double heart shapes that are joined together point to point. Although the hearts have been separated in the needlework, the graph shows how they were originally connected.

× maroon

. cream

▫ lavender

Finished needlework measures 6½″ x 6¼″, for eyeglass case 3⅛″ x 6¼″.

CHICAGO WATER TOWER

(see Color Plate 13)

The Water Tower on Chicago's North Michigan Avenue was a pumphouse built in 1869 under the direction of architect W. W. Boyington. One of the few buildings to survive the Great Fire of 1871, the Gothic edifice with its crenellated towers reminds a viewer of a medieval fortress. Oscar Wilde, who visited Chicago in 1882, called it "a castellated monstrosity with pepper boxes stuck all over it." But he added, "It was not until I had seen the waterworks at Chicago that I realized the wonders of machinery; the rise and fall of the steel rods, the symmetrical motion of great wheels, is the most beautifully rhythmic thing I have ever seen."

The design on the footstool is an adaptation of some of the motifs seen on the building. Even the center medallion is derived from a frame surrounding the window of the second story. The colors used in the design are an addition; the original building is of stone.

The design (one-quarter of which is graphed) is executed on #13 canvas in basketweave with the continental stitch used for outlines and small areas. The two stitches appear identical on the surface of the work. The background is done in mosaic diamond filling, a combination of long and short Bargello stitches that form diamond shapes as they work out. A glance at the pattern will show that a row begins with vertical stitches that cover 2, then 4, then 6, then 4, then 2 threads of the canvas and repeat all across the row. The next row begins with vertical stitches that cover 6, 4, 2, 4, 6 threads and go on across in that fashion. To effect the transition between the beige Bargello background and the dark brown continental stitch outline of the design of the Water Tower, you should follow the instructions described in the Compensation section at the end of the Stitch Dictionary.

Although the design was conceived as a piece of upholstery fabric, it would work well as a pillow and even, if done wholly in basketweave or tent stitch on #5 canvas, as a small rug. The center medallion and crenellations evoke the patterning that is frequently seen in Oriental rugs.

- ■   dark brown

- x   rose

- /   dark rose

- .   blue

- ▫   beige

Finished needlework measures 16¾" x 20".

Background Stitch Pattern

LACE BY MACHINE

(see Color Plate 20)

For centuries, elaborate laces were made only by hand. Hundreds of hours were required to create a few square inches. The Great Exhibition of 1851, in its tribute to the machine-maker's ingenuity, displayed this entirely machine-manufactured lace pattern. Thus, it became possible for large numbers of people to afford the luxurious fashions that had, for so long, been available only to the very rich.

One complete motif has been graphed. The colors in this adaptation of the lace pattern are invented. The blue background, which is a variation of the Leviathan stitch explained in the Stitch Dictionary, might be simplified to the basketweave stitch, if desired. The crosses indicate the off-white basketweave stitch. As stitched on #13 canvas, the design provides an extremely durable surface and would be perfect to cover the chair that a two-year-old uses as a trampoline. It can also be used, of course, for other items that will be more gently treated.

Finished needlework measures 8⅞″ x 9″.

✗ off-white

☐ blue

ROOKERY RAILING

(see Color Plate 5)

At 209 South La Salle Street in Chicago's Loop stands the Rookery, an architectural landmark built in 1886 and designed by the firm of Burnham and Root. The massive elements of the exterior give no clue to the surprise that awaits a visitor to the building—a vast interior court that displays its skeleton of wrought-iron beams and cast-iron columns with open boldness. The ground floor of the court was redesigned by Frank Lloyd Wright in 1906. His additions to the structure include the lightweight, curving stairways with their intricately wrought railings from which this needlepoint design was adapted.

The shades used here are obviously not original. It is only the white tracery of the design that is present in the Rookery; its lacy transparency emphasizes the openness of the space. As can be seen from the color plate, one element has been repeated four times in the sample—a principle that can be applied to many of the designs in this collection. One-half of a single motif has been graphed. The white outline was worked in cross stitch for emphasis, because it might otherwise be overwhelmed by the other shades. This pattern stitched on #14 canvas can be used as a pillow, and it might be especially effective if worked with rug yarn on #5 canvas and made as large as desired.

■ white cross stitch

. light gray

ʋ dark gray

- yellow

╱ light terra cotta

x dark terra cotta

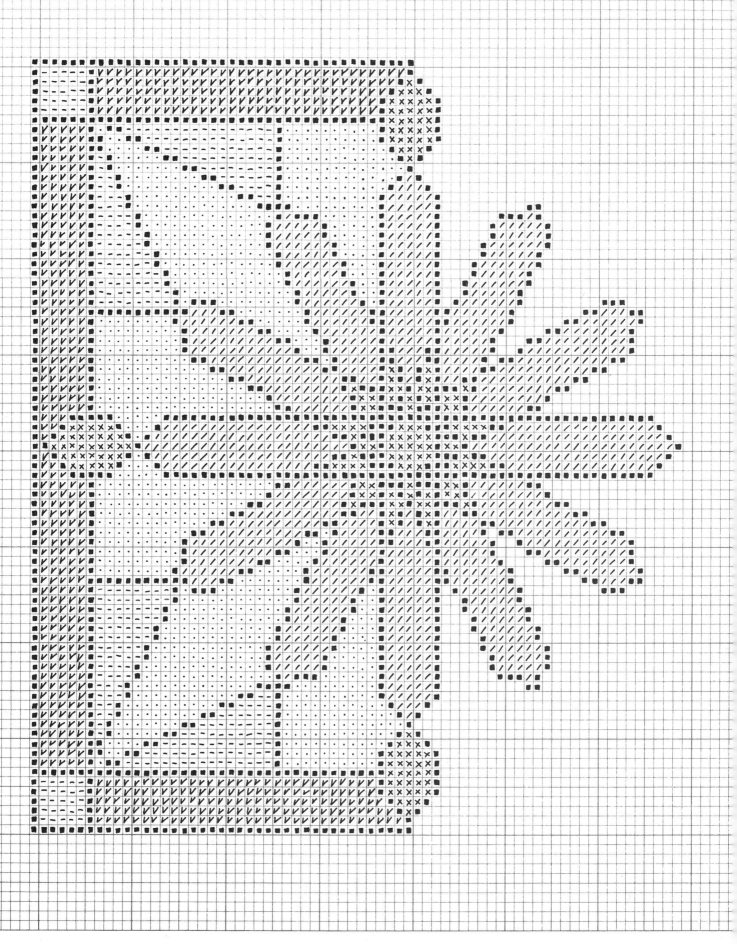

Finished needlework measures 11⅜″ x 11⅜″.

PAINE'S CELERY COMPOUND

(see Color Plate 11)

In an age when access to doctors and hospitals was limited, many people relied on home remedies to cure their afflictions. These might range from something as benign as bathing the nose in warm water to relieve cold symptoms to something as dangerous as the copious quantities of laudanum, an opium derivative, which was freely available for all kinds of ailments. Before the advent of the Food and Drug Administration, medication manufacturers advertised that their potions could do anything from "curing symptoms of decay in liver, kidneys, and bowels" to giving "new life to the nerves." Many of these remedies relied heavily on opium or alcohol or a combination of both, which no doubt relieved symptoms of all kinds of disease while leaving the causes untouched.

The complete pattern for this design has been graphed. The needlepoint was stitched on #13 canvas in continental and basketweave. The work can be framed or made into a pillow to serve as an example of a kind of nineteenth-century Pop Art.

- ■ dark green
- × medium green
- ∕ light green
- • white
- ∨ terra cotta
- ◢ black
- ▫ peach

Finished needlework measures 6⅝" x 12¾".

NATIONAL CASH REGISTER

(see Color Plate 3)

The coming of the industrial age spurred a vast expansion of the retail trade, and with it came the need for a machine that would record and total sales. By 1888 the National Cash Register Company, with 115 employees, was the leading maker of the machine. As the company grew, the cash registers it manufactured became more elaborate until a jeweler was commissioned to design the Dolphin cabinet, from which this stitchery pattern was adapted. Typical of so many industrial goods manufactured both in Great Britain and the United States between the mid-nineteenth century and World War I, the machine was almost enveloped by the functionless rococo ornamentation that animated its bronze surface and, presumably, helped justify a retail price of $100 when it was marketed in 1911.

One-half of the pattern has been graphed. The sample was worked on #14 canvas, which reduces its size considerably. If worked on #10 canvas, the design would be an appropriate size for a sofa pillow, or it might be centered on a piece of #14 canvas and a large margin worked around the edges of the design so that it could be used for upholstery. The dark red design (an addition to emphasize the relief pattern) was done in continental stitches, and the gold background was filled in with basketweave.

✕ dark red

▢ gold

Finished needlework
measures 8½″ x 7⅝″.

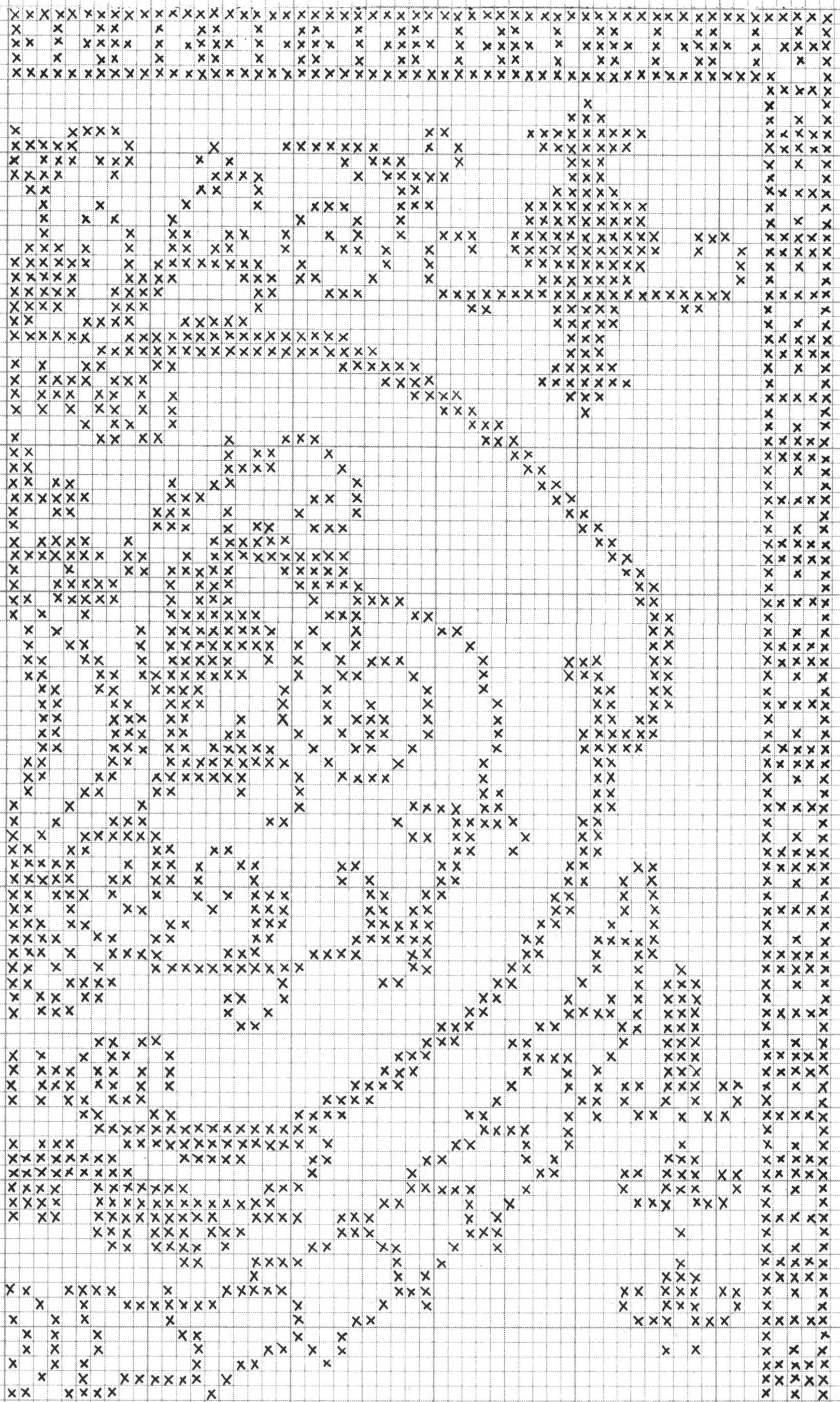

BRAID PATTERN

(see Color Plate 8)

Dressmakers of the last century spent enormous amounts of time elaborating the fussy details that ornamented women's clothes. Along with embroidery and ruffles, they swirled braid, tassels, and ribbons over the yards of fabric that comprised a single garment. One such braid pattern, which flanked a row of central buttons, was this interlace, interpreted here in Bargello stiches. The dress pattern, dating from 1850, was found in the Petit Courrier des Dames, one of the many style catalogues published during the era to provide women with notions of what was fashionable. In this adaptation, the buttons of the original have been replaced by whipped spider webs, a stitch borrowed from crewel embroidery (see the Stitch Dictionary).

One-half of a single motif has been graphed. Although the original colors of the dress are not known (color printing was not invented until decades later), the pattern has been executed in "fawn and bronze," a favorite combination of the era. The brick stitch background in the fawn color has been diagrammed in the Stitch Dictionary, but basketweave or another stitch might be substituted instead. The design was stitched on #13 canvas and can be used for a pillow, a cushion, a bookcover, or a handbag.

| bronze

□ fawn

Finished needlework measures 9½″ x 7¾″.

GINGERBREAD HOUSE

(see Color Plate 16)

Many exteriors of "carpenter Gothic" homes were enlivened by the addition of strategically placed wooden lace: under the roof, on porch railings, or over the surface in an attempt to enhance the look of the structure. This improbable-looking house is an amalgam of six such motifs, and its like has never existed. The bargeboard, the reverse V-shaped form under the roof peak, was derived from a house in South Robbinson, Maine, along with its Gothic window. The first horizontal motif (reading from top to bottom) is an adaptation from a detail at the base of a house in Cambridge, New York; the second, from a bargeboard in Seneca Falls, New York; and the third is related to the corner porch support in a Woodstock Hill, Connecticut, home. The porch railing and columns are from houses in Tolland, Connecticut, and Schoharie, New York, respectively.

The needlepoint is executed in the gray and cream tones advocated by A. J. Downing in his 1850 publication, The Architecture of Country Houses. Downing cites Wordworth's remark, "Upon the whole, the safest color, for general use, is something between a cream and a dust color." Downing says that next to the dusty cream or creamy dust color, which he calls "a quiet fawn color," he likes "a warm gray."

This design is really an example of needlepoint virtuosity and might better be framed than made into something else. If, however, you prefer to turn it into a functional object, its best use would probably be as a five-sided pillow, boxed rather than knife-edged. Welting used around the edge should match the shade of the patterns instead of the background, just to emphasize the line of the roof. Any of the small patterns contained within the house might be used on its own to make a belt or suspenders, for example, or in combination with others in the collection to make pillows or upholstery.

In the needlepointed sample, which was stitched on #13 canvas, each of the designs is separated from the one above it by three rows of gray basketweave or continental stitches. The exception is the "porch" design that is placed six rows below the diamond-shaped motif. For ease of visibility, the graph (one-half of the design) has been divided; the bargeboard and Gothic window are shown as one section (see facing page) and the other designs comprise a separate grouping (see pages 36–37). Here, too, there are three rows of gray below the stitches of the last bargeboard curlicue and the cream stitches at the start of the next design.

✕   cream

◻   gray

Finished needlework measures 14½″ x 20″

(from base to peak).

TOP

WRIGHT'S TILEWORK

(see Color Plate 12)

Every building designed by Frank Lloyd Wright is not necessarily an architectural monument. As a young man working in the Chicago architectural firm of Adler and Sullivan, Wright often had to accede to the wishes of his clients and turn out structures that were neither daring nor particularly innovative. One such ordinary yet pleasant building was the four-story Francis Apartments on South Forrestville designed by Wright in 1895 and demolished in 1971. Covering the first-floor surface of the otherwise brick building was a series of rows of tiled ornamentation, which served as the source of this pattern.

The present colors are not Wright's original ones. The theme of circle upon circle is reminiscent of some of the geometric-styled ornaments designed by Wright's employer, Louis Sullivan. (One complete motif has been graphed. The design can be used in a single row, as was done in the present work stitched on #10 canvas, or as a series, as Wright intended, with one motif directly over another. The pattern can be used for any number of projects, from bookcovers to rugs.

x   light blue

■   dark turquoise

ⱱ   purple

⁑   green

▫   beige

Finished needlework
measures 16½″ x 10″.

MOON, WATERFALL, AND MAPLE

(see Color Plate 13)

In 1862, during the International Exhibition of Art and Industry in London, many Westerners were exposed to Japanese objects for the first time. In that year, too, a shop selling Oriental goods opened in Paris. In succeeding years most of the Impressionists and eventually the public at large recognized the artful serenity of the wood-block prints. From the 1870s to the end of the century, images of all sorts that had in some way been influenced by the Japanese masters were increasingly seen in Great Britain and America.

This needlepoint is an adaptation on #14 canvas of Hiroshige's beautiful print. The works of the artist, one of the last of the great nineteenth-century Japanese printmakers, must surely have been seen by James MacNeill Whistler, Arthur L. Liberty, and those other tastemakers of the later part of the century.

Japanese prints are among the very few works of art that can gracefully be adapted to needlepoint, for they are insistently two-dimensional and so do not require, as do most works of art since the Renaissance, the visual plunge into the depth beyond the surface of the canvas. This was conceived as a framed needlepoint picture, and that is all it should be.

In the print, the transition between the dark indigo blue and palest blue of the sky is made somewhat abruptly. This palest blue is a value very close to white and lighter than the "light blue" used in the waterfall. In the adaptation, I decided to effect the change more subtly, by combining one strand of each of the two blue shades in the needle and stitching several rows of the sky in the resulting "tweed" mixture.

The complete design has been graphed on the following pages. Because the graph of the design is necessarily a complicated one, you might find it easier to work if you color in some of the squares for quick reference.

TOP

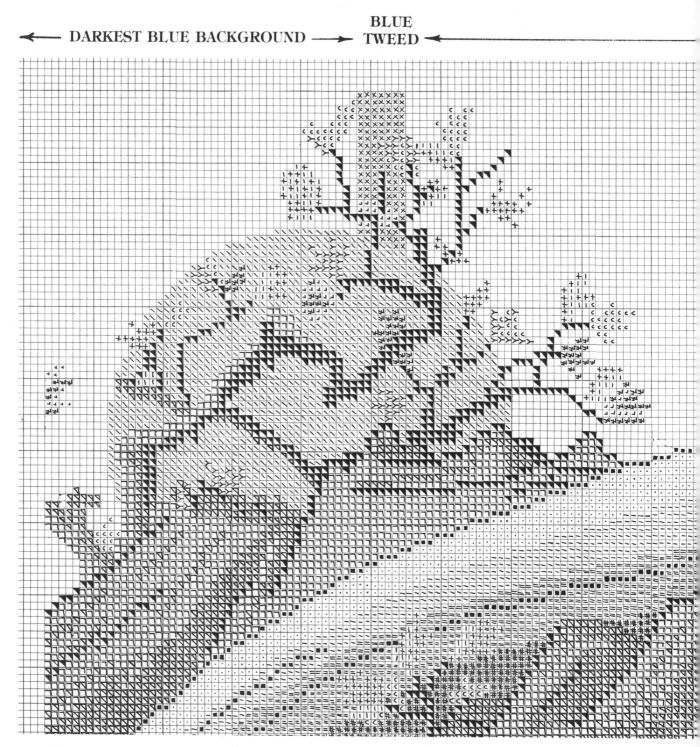

◢ dark brown	⌗ dark medium blue	+ dark green
◿ medium brown	‖ medium blue	- light green
⌐ light brown	ı light blue	Y dark yellow
■ darkest blue	• white	∧ light yellow

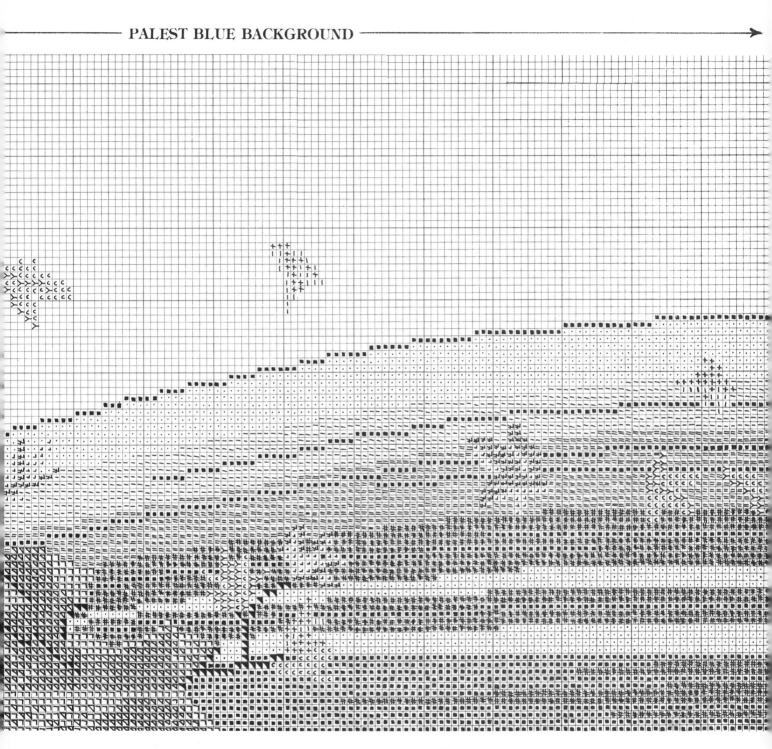

Finished needlework measures 6½″ x 14½″.

4 dark red

ʟ light red

╱ beige

× blue tweed (blend of one strand of darkest blue
   and one strand of palest blue)

VERNEUIL'S SEAHORSE

(see Color Plate 4)

Alphonse Marie Mucha, known primarily for his brilliant posters, was also accomplished in many other media. In 1900, with his associates Maurice Pillard Verneuil and Georges Auriol, he published Combinaisons ornementales se multipliant a l'infini a l'aide du miroir ("Ornamental Combinations Multiplying Themselves to Infinity with the Help of a Mirror"), a collection of sixty color plates of decorative motifs in the style that we have come to call Art Nouveau. Although most of their designs were self-contained works that could stand on their own, the three artists preferred that the motifs be expanded, for they included with each a chart that showed just how any design might be lengthened, widened, or made to turn a corner through the use of a mirror placed at various angles across or alongside the design. The seahorse, tail curled around a floating piece of sinuous seaweed, was conceived by Verneuil, who saw it as one component of a border design and placed several of them in a row in his book.

One complete motif has been graphed. The seahorse, worked on #14 canvas, could be applied to upholstery and clothing and, if executed on larger canvas, might be the right size for a large beach-bag.

x　gray-green

-　taupe

•　white

▫　pale green

Finished needlework measures 9¾" x 11¾".

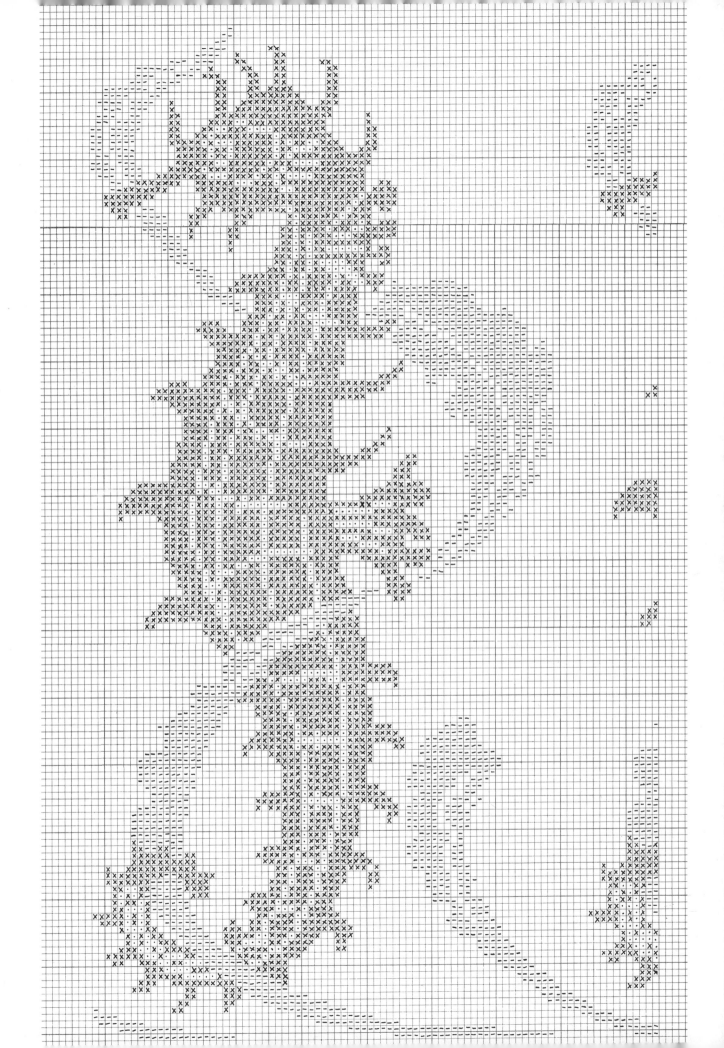

BURHOLME GLASS

(see Color Plate 18)

Although stained glass had been used for centuries in cathedrals and churches, during the nineteenth century many builders turned to it for domestic use because of cheaper manufacturing methods and reduced taxes on glass. One such window, from the cupola of Burholme, the estate of the Ryerss family in Philadelphia, was the source of this design. Built in 1859, the home is now maintained as a museum (and its grounds as a park).

The pattern (one-quarter of which is graphed) was executed on #10 canvas. It might be used in multiples on a smaller-mesh canvas to make a large project, such as a pillow or upholstery fabric. If the design is executed just as in the sample, the fabric of a matching color might be stitched around all four sides to make a cushion or pillow of whatever size you choose.

The continental stitch was used for the outlines and for small areas, and the basketweave stitch was used for the background.

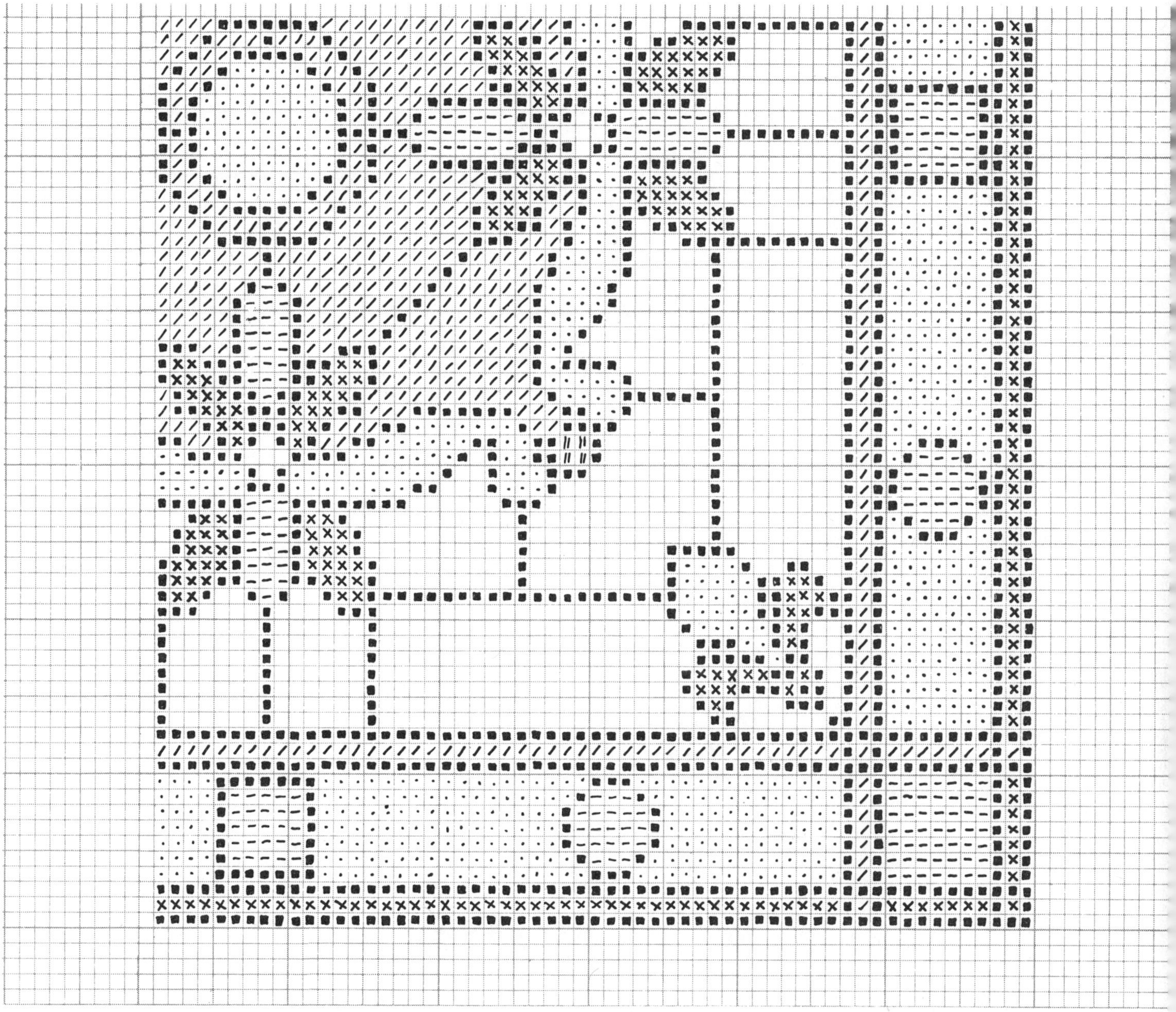

- ■ black
- / blue
- • light yellow
- × dark green
- - light green
- ‖ red
- ▫ dark yellow

Finished needlework measures 10″ x 10″.

BUTTERFLY PROFILE

(see Color Plate 14)

Made in France in 1900 by Feuillâtre, the Art Nouveau gold filigree brooch that inspired this needlepoint represents the esprit that also animated many English artists—Aubrey Beardsley being perhaps the best known of them—in the decade before the turn of the century. The juxtaposition of a pale ivory profile and the brilliantly enameled butterfly wings set with moonstones is unsettling, even irrational. We are reminded, almost against our will, of swiftly glimpsed images not found in nature that we only half remember after pulling away from the tentacles of our dreams, or our nightmares.

The complete design has been graphed. The needlepoint was worked on #10 canvas and would make a striking pillow. The pattern would also be useful for other projects that require hard wear because it is worked in the basketweave stitch.

Finished needlework measures 14½″ x 11½″.

■ gold

× royal blue

╱ black

• white

⌃ light blue

⌐ green

+ violet

‖ light gray

◻ pink

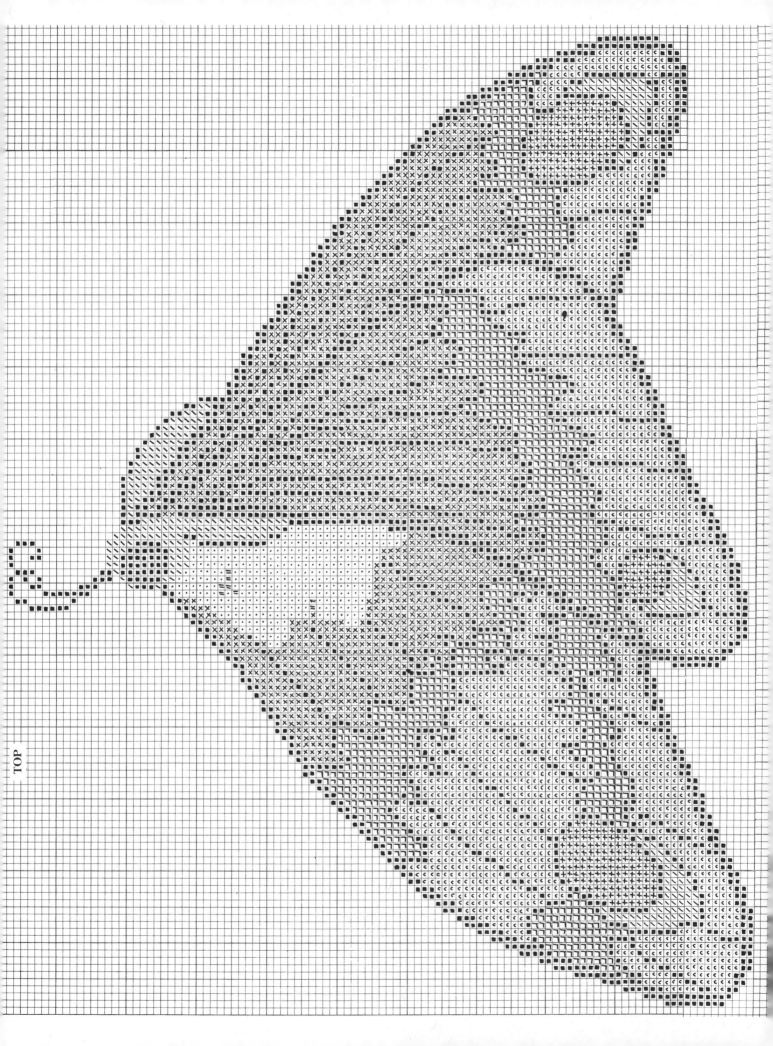

TOP

WILLIAM MORRIS'S CARPET

(see Color Plate 10)

William Morris was a poet, printer, painter, architect, interior designer, weaver, politician, and Socialist. He was, in the words of one biographer, "an angry young man and an angry old man, but he always knew what he was angry about." Much of what appalled him was the tastelessness, shoddiness, and avariciousness of Victorian society, where the many toiled for the benefit of the few. He founded his firm of Morris, Marshall, Faulkner & Co. (later Morris & Co.) in an effort to create objects of superior craftsmanship and design that would combat the ugliness and shabby manufacture that he saw all around him. Morris wanted to propagate the notion that objects should be honestly made of the finest materials and workmanship. His firm turned out wallpapers, stained glass, rugs, textiles, furnishings, and beautifully printed and bound editions both of classics and of Morris's own literary works.

This carpet pattern was designed by Morris, though it was manufactured by the Heckmonwike Company in Yorkshire. It was woven in 32-inch widths that were used as stair carpeting or seamed together for use in larger rooms. Although the colors here are not the ones Morris originally used, they are derived from his palette, for he preferred the look of natural dyes to those of chemical origin. One complete motif has been graphed. The design was stitched on #14 canvas.

■ teal blue

. green

⌐ light copper

∕ cream

Finished needlework measures 9¼″ x 8⅞″.

copper
tulip

copper
lily

copper
tulip

copper
tulip

cream
lily

cream
tulip

EASTLAKE'S PARQUET FLOOR

(see Color Plate 1)

Charles L. Eastlake, a nephew of the president of the Royal Academy, wrote his <u>Hints on Household Taste</u> in 1868 in an effort "to suggest some fixed principles of taste for the popular guidance of those who are not accustomed to hear such principles defined." In the book he inveighed against "monstrous notion[s]" and sought to advise "Materfamilias" about how to discriminate "between good and bad design in those articles of daily use which we are accustomed to see around us. . . ."

One of the designs he advocated was this adaptation of a pattern for parquet flooring. The lavender, purple, and white used in the needlepoint is an addition, derived from the shades of a tasteful American woman's dress of 1872, the year Eastlake's book was published in the United States. The pattern, as can be seen from the chart (one complete motif has been graphed), is a combination of Bargello and basketweave stitches, and was stitched on #14 canvas. The rigorous geometry of this design would work for a pillow or the upholstery of a small piece of furniture.

| dark lavender
, lavender
ʃ dark purple
∕ white

Finished needlework measures 9¼″ x 7″.

WILLIAM MORRIS'S CHINTZ

(see Color Plate 7)

English artist William Morris, revolted by shoddily produced Victorian geegaws and ornamentation, founded his firm to produce "murals, architectural carvings, stained glass, metal work and furniture . . . of a genuine and beautiful character. . . ." Though Morris was influenced to a large degree by the Gothic predilections of John Ruskin, his wallpapers and textiles were animated by a taste for the beauty revealed naturally in wildflowers and plants. "Daffodil" was the name given by Morris to this 1891 chintz pattern. Some of Morris's minute detail has had to be amended in this adaptation. The curvilinear motifs disclose an influence of Art Nouveau that was then beginning to affect English interior design.

The pattern (a complete motif has been graphed on the following pages) was executed on #14 canvas and should probably not be worked larger because the detail might be coarsened. The pattern would be lovely used, as Morris meant it to be, on a large surface, to upholster a chair, an ottoman, or, if one is truly ambitious, a love seat.

■	white	v	olive green	-	light gold
×	red	‖	medium gold	.	black
/	light green	◤	dark gold	▫	charcoal gray

Finished needlework measures 8¼″ x 13⅝″.

LITHOGRAPHED FLOWERS

(see Color Plate 2)

As printing techniques grew more sophisticated, lithography and other processes involving the use of several colors were increasingly employed for the specialized art journals that proliferated in Europe and the United States during the latter part of the nineteenth century. One such journal for artists and architects, Dekorative Vorbilder ("Decorative Patterns"), published in Stuttgart, Germany, from 1889 to 1929, regularly carried designs that might be used for stained glass, tiles, or other decorative architectural elements. Typical was this arrangement of leaves and flowers reproduced in the needlepoint sample in shades very close to the originals featured in this journal in 1900.

One-quarter of the design has been graphed. As executed on #13 canvas, it is the perfect size for a pillow. A mitered border can be made with upright long Bargello stitches covering four threads along the sides and tapering to three, two, and one threads in the corners. If you want to change the color scheme, it would be best to combine gentle, pale shades of the preferred hues to preserve the spirit of the original design.

Finished needlework measures 12″ x 12″.

Border Pattern

× green

▪ violet

⌐ brown

. white

▫ beige

Color Plate 1. Eastlake's Parquet Floor

Color Plate 2. Lithographed Flowers

Color Plate 3. National Cash Register

Color Plate 4. Verneuil's Seahorse

Color Plate 5. Rookery Railing

Color Plate 6. Beardsley's Botanic Garden

Color Plate 8. Braid Pattern

Color Plate 7. William Morris's Chintz

Color Plate 9. Fernery

Color Plate 10. William Morris's Carpet

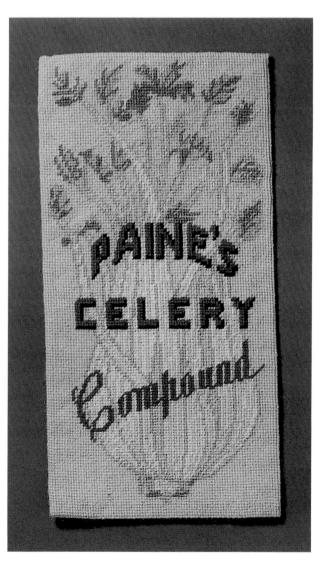

Color Plate 11. Paine's Celery Compound

Color Plate 12. Clockwise: Wright's Tilework bookcover; New Haven Bracket evening bag; Cast-Iron Flower pincushion; Vanderbilt Balcony belt; Victorian Beadwork belt; Shell of Iron lingerie case.

Color Plate 13. Clockwise: The Rising Sun tabard; Chicago Water Tower footstool; Newport Cabinetwork pillow; South Kensington Grillwork eyeglass case; Moon, Waterfall, and Maple framed needlepoint picture.

Color Plate 14. Butterfly Profile

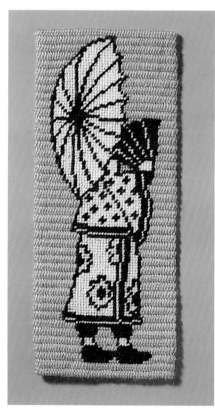

Color Plate 15. Oriental Figure

Color Plate 16. Gingerbread House

Color Plate 18. Burholme Glass

Color Plate 17. Crystal Palace Carpet

Color Plate 19. Victorian Appliqué

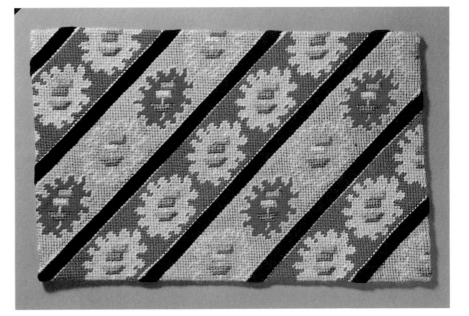

Color Plate 20. Lace by Machine

Color Plate 21. Stickley's Scarf

Color Plate 22. Folk-Art Scrolls

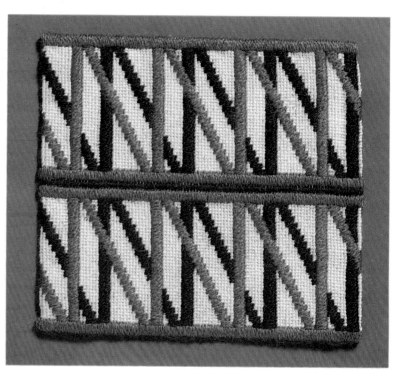

Color Plate 23. Railroad Bridge

RAILROAD BRIDGE

(see Color Plate 23)

With the development of the railroads, the mobility of the ordinary citizen of the last century increased a thousandfold. Not only could he travel from one end of his country to the other, but he might also commute to work every day from outlying areas. Thus, suburban development, supplanting a profusion of small farms, was born.

Many of the early railroad bridges that spanned the great rivers were constructed of wood. One such was the inspiration for this pattern. Located at Orrton, about fifty miles from Philadelphia, the bridge crossed the Schuylkill River and allowed the train to make the run to Reading in the 1880s. The wooden span and its supporting members on one side seemed to be echoed in shadow on the other, and that is how the lines have been rendered in this pattern.

The design is executed on #14 canvas in a combination of basketweave or continental and Bargello stitches. You can see from the graph (which includes a complete motif) that the Bargello has to be lifted slightly to permit the basketweave stitches to slide underneath them, because occasionally both stitches occupy the same mesh. I have filled in the basketweave symbols in only one area of the graph in order to give clarity to the Bargello pattern. But all empty squares within the design should be stitched in basketweave, or if you prefer, the continental.

This pattern might be of particular interest to someone whose initials include the letter "N". It can be used to make any article for which a heavy fabric would be suitable.

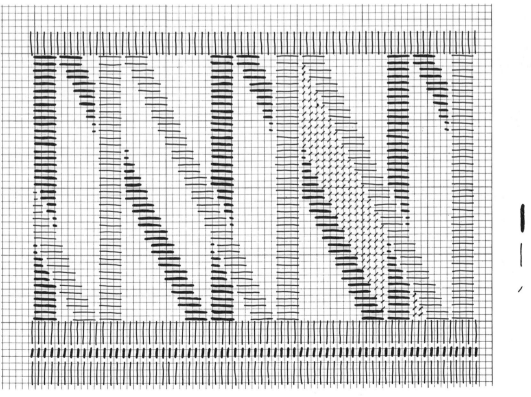

| dark brown
| medium brown
⟋ beige basketweave stitch

Finished needlework measures 7¼″ x 6½″.

CRYSTAL PALACE CARPET

(see Color Plate 17)

This pattern is derived from an engraving in a special issue of the Art-Journal, the illustrated catalogue of the Crystal Palace Exhibition of 1851. Designed for a carpet manufacturing company of Leeds, England, the rug pattern was reproduced in the catalogue in black and white only; thus, the present coloration is a modern adaptation of some popular hues on the Victorian palette.

The complete center motif and one-quarter of the border have been graphed. The sample was stitched on #10 canvas, which is an adequate size for a pillow or a footstool covering, but if worked on #5 canvas with three or four strands of Persian yarn in the needle, it would be a wonderful small rug before the fireplace, in a hall, at a bedside, or anywhere else a small rug is welcome.

MEDALLION

▯	maroon	Ϟ	dark violet
#	dark pink	L	light violet
‖	dark medium pink	÷	white
I	light medium pink	M	mauve
X	lightest pink	⌐	light green
Y	dark yellow	c	gray-green
+	light yellow	V	medium green
B	dark blue	▮	taupe
∧	medium blue	Λ	grass green
⊦	light blue	◢	medium gold

BORDER

–	light gold	▮	taupe
◁	dark gold	#	dark pink
/	light green	‖	dark medium pink
▪	dark green	V	medium green
.	off-white	Λ	grass green

Finished needlework measures 11¾″ x 14″.

VICTORIAN BEADWORK

(see Color Plate 12)

Beading was a form of ornamentation much beloved by late nineteenth-century women who used it for knitting, crocheting, and. as in this sample, needlepoint canvas. The design is a twentieth-century adaptation of an 1847 British pattern published in The Illuminated Book of Needlework by Mrs. Henry Owen and the Countess of Wilton. Mrs. Owen believed that, "Slippers in this style are much approved," although she preferred that a combination of gray, blue, white, and scarlet be used for the pattern instead of the present two, gray and dark red.

The complete motif has been graphed. The sample belt was stitched on #14 canvas using Persian yarn and gray glass seed beads that are widely sold in craft shops. (The **X**'s on the graph indicate the bead stitches.) First the beads were stitched onto the canvas one at a time in continental stitch following the pattern just as with yarn. But, in place of yarn, the beads were sewn with three strands of dark red buttonhole silk twist for added strength and flexibility. After each stitch, a new bead is threaded onto the needle. The dark red background was stitched with Persian yarn in the continental after the beaded pattern was completed.

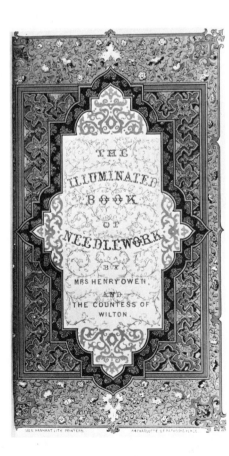

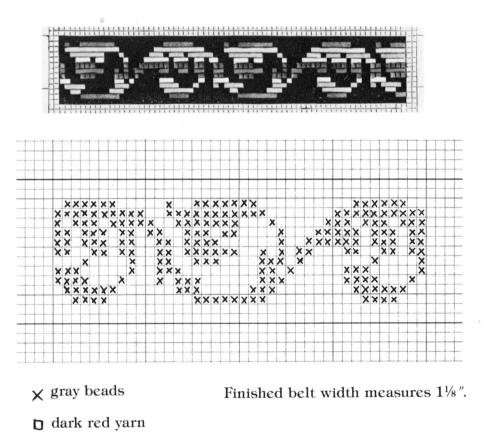

✗ gray beads

◻ dark red yarn

Finished belt width measures 1⅛″.

VICTORIAN APPLIQUÉ

(see Color Plate 19)

To give some idea of the kind of needlepoint that was done by stitchers of the Victorian era more than a century ago, the pattern shown below is a reproduction of one that was advocated in The Illuminated Book of Needlework (described on the opposite page). These directions for making the pattern were given by Mrs. Owen and the Countess: "The pattern illustrated in this Plate may be extended to any size. The yellow outlines are first worked in wool, and the remaining portions also, though in colours, according to those given in the pattern. The pattern being so far completed, you must then work over the yellow wool with yellow silk. The velvet should be placed between the straight rows of yellow silk, and fixed at each of the edges. The above instructions it is hoped will be found sufficient to give the reader, or rather worker, the necessary clue to this rich and elegant description of work."

The complete motif has been graphed. Because of the scarcity of silk yarn in many contemporary shops, this "worker" elected to use embroidery floss to "work over" the yellow wool in cross stitch. The design was executed on #10 canvas. The velvet ribbon was hemmed down on both sides between the yellow rows just as the women advised. The principle of appliqué on needlepoint canvas seems an appealing one, and if you wish, a motif can be cut from a piece of upholstery or drapery fabric and a simple design, like checks or stripes, stitched around it. Blocking such a canvas can be a problem. You should be especially careful that the hemming stitches on the appliqué do not pull out.

■   yellow

x   dark blue

/   light gray

−   light blue

=   red

L   lavender

⅃   dark lavender

‖   dark gray

•   white

⌃   light green

Y   dark green

Ҡ   black ribbon

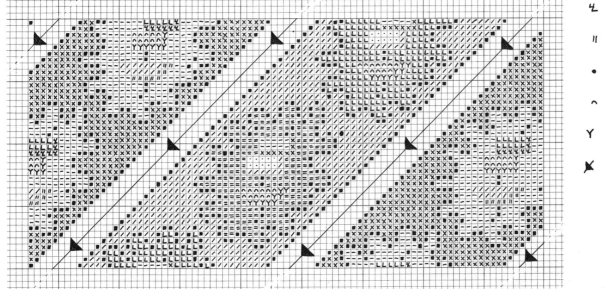

Finished needlework measures 15″ x 9⅛″.

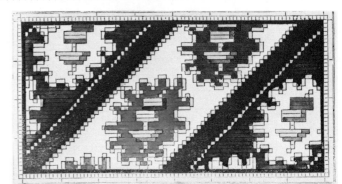

CAST-IRON FLOWER

(see Color Plate 12)

During the second half of the nineteenth century, many merchants preferred cast-iron architecture for their stores because it permitted the construction of large, street-facing windows in which to display their wares. Then, too, the use of thin, iron support columns permitted interior ceilings to rise to new heights and freed much more floor space for the sale of merchandise.

Usually, it was only the façade that received the cast-iron skin; the sides and back of most buildings were made of brick. The structure at 94 Mercer Street in New York City was an exception. The cast iron from which this flower-like form has been adapted was actually the rear entrance. The front of the building, which dates to 1884, faces Broadway.

The complete pattern has been graphed. The hues of this design are an invention. Though the needlepoint, stitched on #14 canvas, was turned into a pincushion here, the small piece of circular canvas could also be used as a coaster, and it might be fun to turn the same design into a set of coasters of different colors. Another possibility would be to make a pillow in quickpoint.

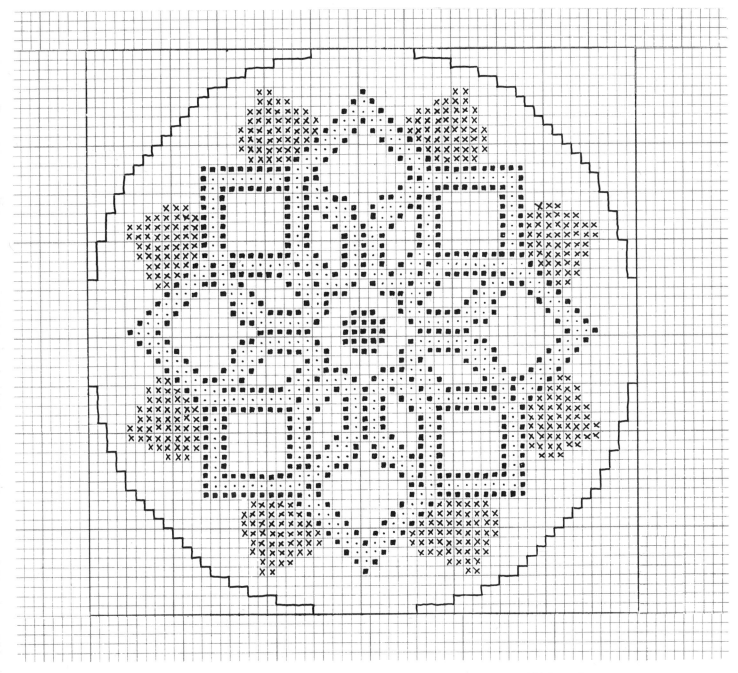

Pincushion measures 4¼" in diameter.

■ avocado green

× khaki

• cream

▫ gold

THE RISING SUN

(see Color Plate 13)

The public house, or pub, has been a British institution for decades. More than just a place where intoxicating beverages are sold, pubs often serve as a combination of community center, lodge hall, and debating arena for millions of Britons. One such public house, built in 1897, is The Rising Sun, which still stands on Tottenham Court Road in London. Housed in a small, pale, four-story Flamboyant Gothic building encrusted with scrollwork, the pub looks as if it had been a last-minute, ground-floor addition to a slightly dusty, dotty, spired wedding cake.

One-quarter of the design has been graphed. The spires and scrollwork of The Rising Sun have been amended somewhat in translation, and color has been added. I chose to make the pattern into a tabard, a kind of tunic, but it could also be used in upholstery, or on a telephone-book cover. The design was stitched on #13 canvas.

×   dark brown

■   blue-green

•   gold

□   terra cotta

Finished needlework measures 11½ " x 31½ ".

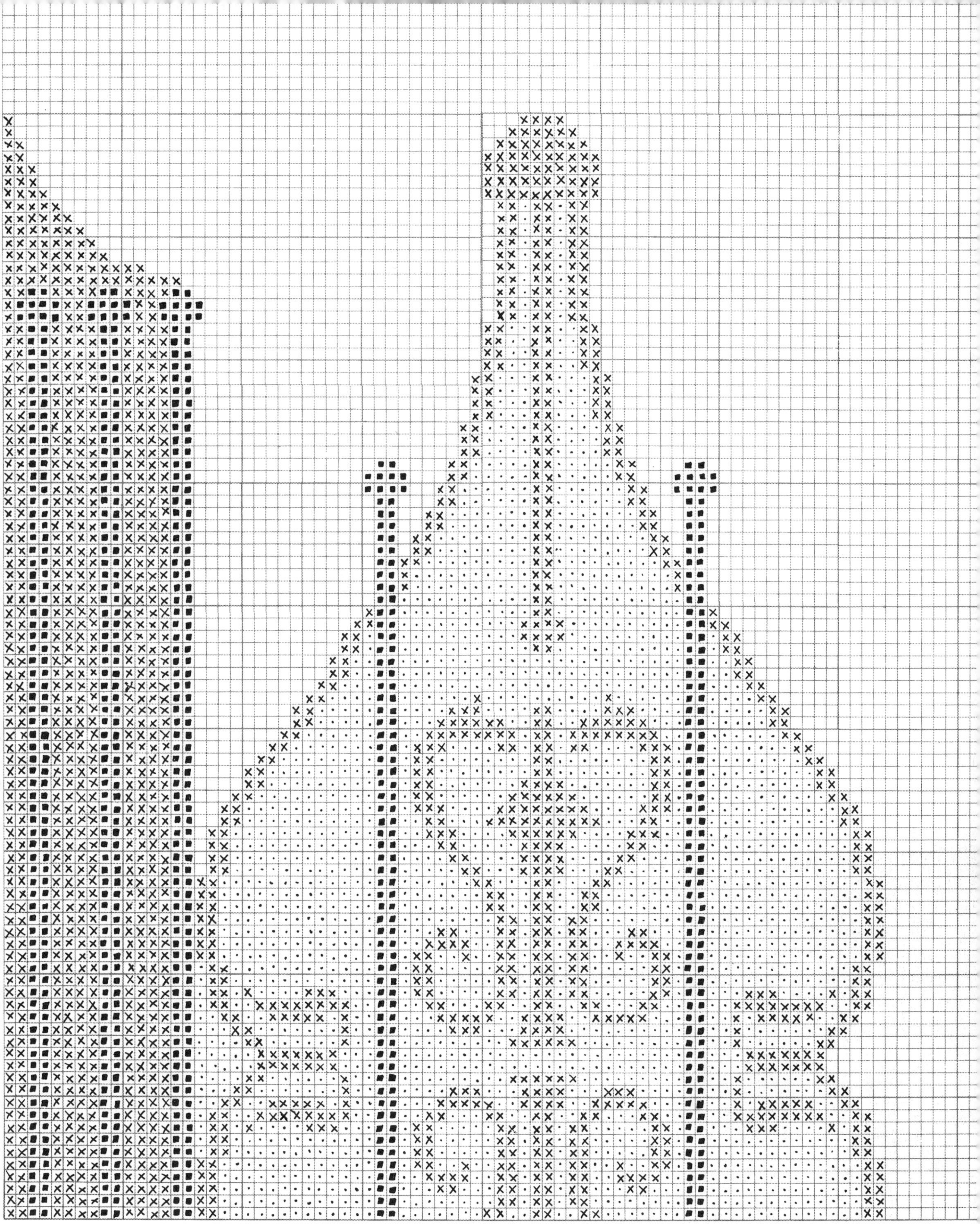

NEWPORT CABINETWORK

(see Color Plate 13)

Newport, Rhode Island, was not only a harbor of great importance in the seventeenth and eighteenth centuries, but it was the site of substantial summer homes almost since its founding. Even before the American Revolution, families from as far away as Charleston, South Carolina, came regularly to Newport to avoid the "miasmas" and concomitant fevers that would attack during the unbearably hot, humid summer months. After the mid-nineteenth century, when the town had begun to lose its importance as a commercial center, new industrialists, many of them enormously wealthy "robber barons," began to select Newport for their summer "cottages," which were, in fact, huge mansions of the most ornate design and expensive execution. One such overgrown cottage was the W. Watts Sherman house, built in 1874, for which Henry Hobson Richardson was the architect.

Another important architect, Stanford White, who at one time worked as Richardson's apprentice, designed the interiors of the house. The work on a cabinet in the library, a long room full of intricately wrought dark wood, was the source of the design adapted here.

One-half of the design has been graphed. A combination of short Bargello stitches and basketweave on #14 canvas, the needlepoint uses shades that are, naturally, an invention. Only one section of basketweave has been filled in on the chart to show how the Bargello and smaller stitches work together. The rest of the color scheme can be seen on the color plate, but I hope that you will prefer to use one that can be uniquely personal. Although this design was used for a small pillow, one considerably larger might be made by repeating the pattern twice or four times.

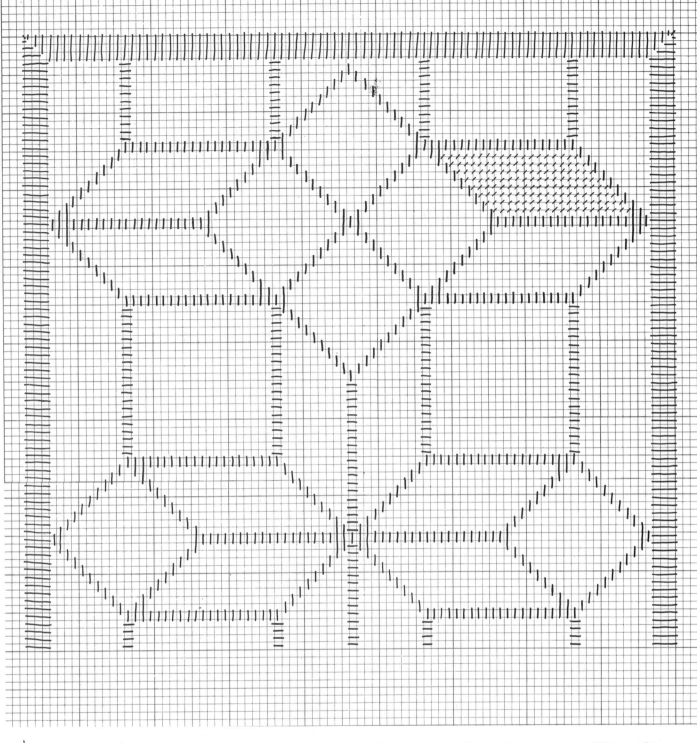

| blue Bargello stitch

/ off-white basketweave stitch

Finished needlework measures 6¾″ x 10″.

FOLK-ART SCROLLS

(see Color Plate 22)

People who were locked in the struggle to establish a nation prior to the mid-nineteenth century and wrest farmland from virgin forest and prairie had little time for much entertainment. After mid-century, householders began to use their time and talent for their own amusement as they created "crazy quilts" no longer for warmth but for show, whirligigs that performed air-powered motions of their own in addition to telling how the wind was blowing, and furniture that was painted in fantastic ways. In short, the phenomenon that we refer to as folk art reached its zenith a century ago.

Folk-artist John Schol was a German immigrant who lived in Potter County, Pennsylvania, and made his living as a carpenter. During his spare time, Schol made a series of fantastic carvings, some of which were over six feet high. The piece shown below inspired this pattern.

One-quarter of the design has been graphed. The needlepoint is executed on #13 canvas in a series of long, uneven Bargello stitches that, when used next to one another, resemble a kind of coarse weaving. Because of the long stitches, this design might not be suitable for projects that would be subjected to a lot of hard use. The pattern would work as the center of a pillow surrounded by fabric on four sides, or on a smaller canvas, #16 or #18, in multiples for an entire pillow surface.

 white

blue

tan

Finished needlework measures 8¼" x 8¼".

NEW HAVEN BRACKET

(see Color Plate 12)

An alert observer who spends any length of time in the center of many of our older cities can often spot memorable remnants of nineteenth-century architecture. Although many older buildings have been "modernized" almost beyond redemption, occasionally one can find a business or residential building that has been well maintained over the years and proudly wears its heritage of stained or leaded glass, lacy ironwork, or ornate scrolls. The business district of New Haven, Connecticut, is a place still full of such architectural elements, but it is often necessary to look up past the storefronts to find the worthy survivors from the past.

One New Haven building that has stayed intact is a former residence on Temple Street; it was converted into offices by Yale University. A wood-frame building now painted a light terra cotta and tan, the house has a large overhanging roof supported by elaborately contrived brackets. One of the brackets served as the inspiration for this design.

Half of the pattern has been graphed. The work was done on #18 canvas with single strands of DMC Perlé cotton for a silky sheen (see page 85). Canvas this size is too small, perhaps, for many projects (and difficult for the eyes, too) but lends itself beautifully to tiny items such as this evening purse. If worked on larger canvas, #10, for example, with margins larger than those indicated on the pattern, a pillow or upholstery fabric could be made of the pattern. The colors and background stitches might be changed, too, for a completely different effect. The gold in the design was worked in continental stitches, and the small black stitches edging the gold were done in basketweave. The graph indicated the pattern for the Bargello stitches that were used on the body of the purse.

x gold

◻ black

Finished purse is approximately 7″ x 6½″.

Background Stitch Pattern

ORIENTAL FIGURE

(see Color Plate 15)

The love of exotic elements and all things Oriental that began with the early Western fascination with Japanese prints extended outward in all directions until it eventually reached the area of graphic design. The figure shown here is a printer's filler from an 1889 book titled Our Home, or, The Key to a Nobler Life by C. E. Sargent. The American volume was full of wise saws about "Resolutions and Individual Rules of Life" and homilies on "Courage to Meet Life's Duties." Presumably the book was designed as a gift to be given by, say, a stern but loving aunt to a graduating scholar of tenuous ethics to remind him of his "Responsibilities." This little figure was one of a number of small designs that included a parrot, a fan, and a Chinese junk on the presentation page of the volume.

The connection between moral obligation and a Japanese image is, at best, dubious. The figure with its face hidden by umbrella and fan is, however, one more link in the chain of faceless figures that have graced American folk images from the Sunbonnet Sue of patchwork quilts to the little girl on Old Dutch Cleanser whose face was concealed behind the starched whiteness of her hat.

The needlepoint was done on #14 canvas in the black and white of the graphic design on a rose background, but you may prefer to do the figure in color. The X's on the graph represent the black continental stitches, and the rest of the figure is worked in white basketweave. A row of such figures might be appealing on a pillow, a bookcover, or a vest. Another stitch can substitute for the knotted stitch used on the background.

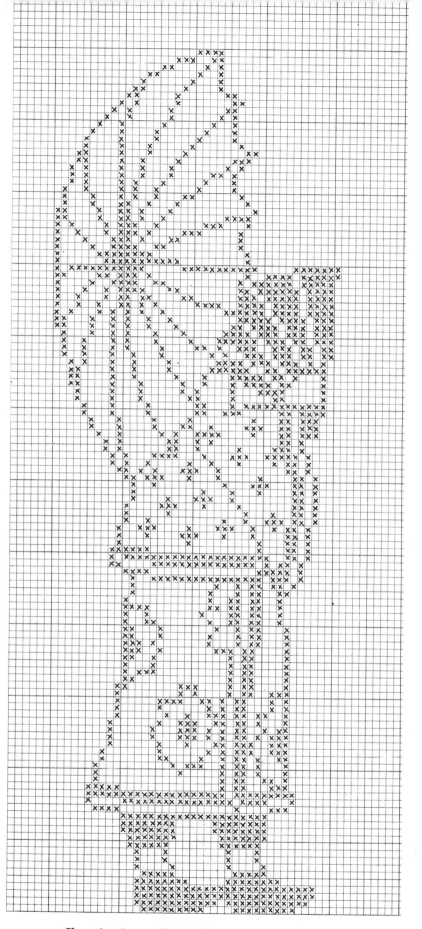

x   black

 white

background in
pink knotted stitch

Finished needlework measures 3¾" x 9".

STICKLEY'S SCARF

(see Color Plate 21)

Gustave Stickley was a cabinetmaker heavily influenced by the aesthetic aims of William Morris and the Arts and Crafts movement in England. He established his own furniture factory in Syracuse around 1899 and advocated "honesty and sincerity" in architecture and "greater strength and beauty" in furniture. He created his Craftsman magazine in 1903 to serve as a forum for his ideas. In it, he published his philosophical and sociological notions along with house plans and pictures of interiors and household furnishings of every sort. Stickley wanted to return the fireplace to the living room, from which it had been banished after the development of central heating, because he believed it would "increase social happiness." He also thought that the nation's health would be improved by the addition of sleeping porches onto homes.

Even household linens received Stickley's scrupulous attention. Homespun fabrics were the most desirable, and natural shades were considered most attractive. This pattern of ginko leaves and stems (one-half of which is graphed) is one of Stickley's designs for a table scarf. It is stitched on #13 canvas in shades Stickley advocated. The small design worked on #10 canvas would make a nice handbag or could be repeated several times for use as a pillow or upholstery. The stitches used in the design can be found in the Stitch Dictionary.

Finished needlework measures 6¾″ x 5⅛″.

■ dark green cross stitch

. white continental stitch

↑↓ light green interlocking
Gobelin stitch

□ tan true cross stitch

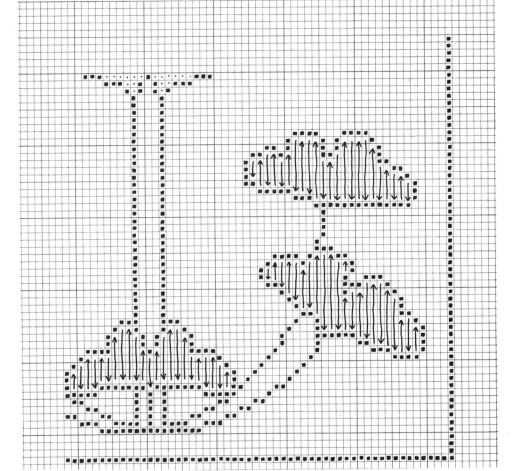

BEARDSLEY'S BOTANIC GARDEN

(see Color Plate 6)

Aubrey Beardsley is perhaps best known for his illustrations of such works as Oscar Wilde's Salome and Malory's Le Morte D'Arthur. While strongly influenced by Japanese art, Beardsley's work exhibits an erotic surrealism that hints at the decadence many contemporaries believed was rampant in the decade just before the turn of the century. Beardsley worked primarily in black and white, the shades used in this adaptation of flowers from a book cover design that he executed in about 1892.

One complete motif has been graphed (see following pages). The flowers and leaves are worked with black yarn in continental stitch on #14 canvas. The white ground is done in the brick stitch that is diagrammed in the Stitch Dictionary. Because two stitch patterns confront each other at the edge of the design, you should consult the Compensation section of the Stitch Dictionary to learn how to maintain the sharp, clear edges of both black and white areas.

Although there is no reason why this pattern, like many of the others, cannot be used for anything one wants to make of it, in whole or in part, its graphic quality might be especially effective on valences behind which hang white, filmy curtains similar to the drapery worn by many figures in Beardsley's illustrations.

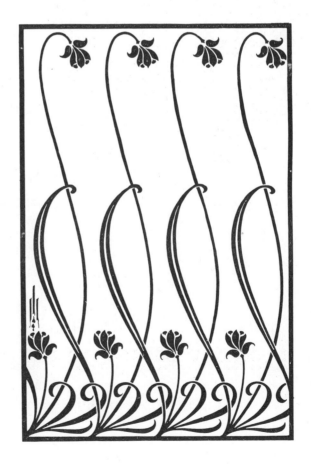

X black   □ white

Finished needlework measures 11¾″ x 14⅞″.

VANDERBILT BALCONY

(see Color Plate 12)

The Chateau de Blois, on Fifth Avenue between 57th and 58th streets was the New York home of Cornelius Vanderbilt II. Now the site of the Bergdorf Goodman emporium, the house was so vast that it supposedly required a staff of thirty to maintain it properly. Architect George B. Post, a protégé of Richard Morris Hunt, designed the red brick and gray limestone structure, which was begun in 1880 and was still being added on to in 1894. The only surviving elements of the building, which was torn down in 1927, are the huge north gates that have been relocated at Central Park and 105th Street.

This pattern was adapted from a horizontal band of stonework that formed the third-floor balcony above the "everyday" entrance to the home on 57th Street. The opposite entrance faced Grand Army Plaza and was graced by an elaborate porte cochere. I stitched this needlepoint on #10 canvas in shades derived from the materials used in the building's construction. One complete motif has been graphed. If a smaller-scale belt is desired, you might work the same design on #13 or #14 canvas until the necessary length is reached.

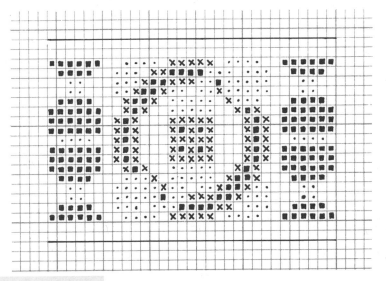

Belt width measures 2″.

▪	white	•	gray
x	red	□	black

FERNERY

(see Color Plate 9)

The Great Exhibition of 1851 displayed many products manufactured with the use of the new machines. Among them was this carpet pattern of ferns that was described by the Exhibition's official catalogue as "one of the most graceful productions of the woods and hedgerows, and as seen worked out in this carpet in shades of the liveliest green, nothing can be more ornamental."

The design was stitched on #14 canvas and might lose some of its grace if worked larger. The pattern (see the following pages) might be seen to its best advantage if used as upholstery fabric.

	dark green		|| medium green		• pale green
	x dark medium green			light medium green		◻ brown

Finished needlework measures 12″ x 7⅜″.

SHELL OF IRON

(see Color Plate 12)

This shell pattern ornaments a cast-iron column base on a building at 400 Lafayette Street in New York City, still elegant and graceful despite its peeling paint. The delicacy of this pattern may suggest why nineteenth-century real estate magnates often preferred cast iron over any other material for the façades of their buildings. Iron might be cast in any shape and in any style, so a builder could select from among scores of elements and have his choices assembled in any way he liked. Since the iron castings were portable, a resident of Savannah or San Francisco could order his "building" in New York and have it sent to him within a relatively short time.

I chose to do this design in pinks, greens, and white. One motif has been graphed, and the pattern might be worked in a series of rows separated by narrow bands of stitches other than the Bargello variation shown here. It could be used for a handbag or a footstool and might be done on canvas larger or smaller than the #14 used for this design.

- ◼ dark pink
- ⌄ medium pink
- • light pink
- – white
- / light green
- ✗ medium green
- ◻ dark green

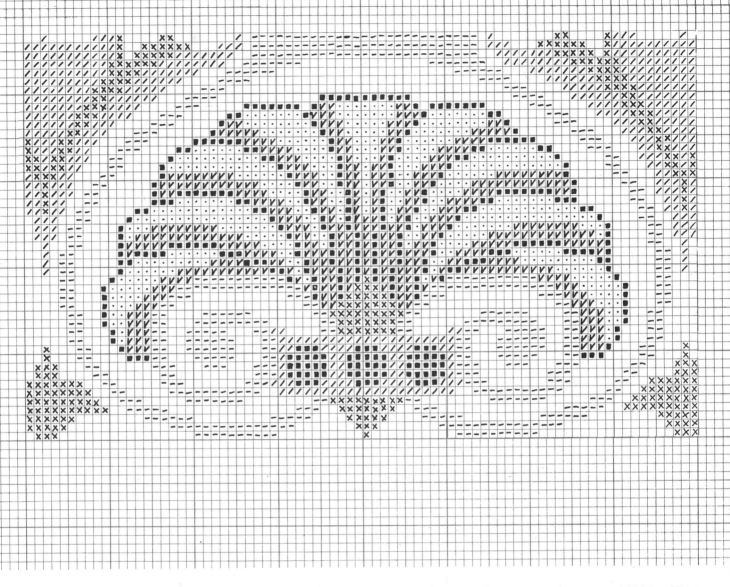

Finished needlework measures 10¾″ x 15½″ for case measuring 10¾″ x 7¾″.

Background
Stitch Pattern

Instructions for Finishing Projects

The last pin has been taken off the blocking board, each corner of the finished canvas measures exactly 90°, and the center of the canvas is taut and flat. If you stitched for hours to produce a canvas for framing, your work is now finished. Bring it to the framer's and let him do the rest. If, however, you want to put your labors to another use, your work is far from completed. No matter what your needlepoint will become, the first steps in dealing with it are very much alike.

Take one side of the canvas that was just removed from the blocking board and fold the unworked edge back against the wrong side of the finished work from corner to corner. Pin it down if you like. Then take a standard sewing needle threaded with sewing cotton (or cotton-and-polyester) that matches the predominant color of the needlepoint and use small running stitches to baste down the unworked canvas about one-half inch from the edge. Check the front of the work to make sure the cotton stitches don't show through. The basting stitches should be strengthened with a backstitch every three inches or so. When you've gone from one corner to the next, stop, end the stitching with a knot, and cut off the thread.

Hold in your hand the masking-taped edge of the canvas that you have just sewn and keep it away from the surface of the wrong side of the canvas. With your other hand, cut away the masking tape and unworked canvas edge one-half inch below the running stitches you have just made. There should now be an inch of unworked canvas sewn down along one edge of your piece of needlepoint (one-half inch before the running stitches, plus a half-inch margin beyond them). There are three sides left with unworked canvas sticking out around them. Perform the same steps around the three remaining sides: fold down, pin, stitch invisibly, trim.

What should remain after all four sides have been hemmed down is a piece of needlepoint with no unworked canvas threads showing at the edges. On the wrong side there should be one inch of unworked canvas firmly stitched down along every edge.

Now, place the canvas on the lining fabric you purchased earlier. It is usual for the lining to match the predominant color of the needlework, but if you want yours to contrast, fine. The important thing to keep in mind is that the lining should not show through on the right side of the work. Use the hemmed needlepoint piece as a pattern and cut a rectangle of lining fabric one inch larger than the needlepoint on all four sides. That means that if your finished piece of needlepoint measures 8″ by 10″, the lining fabric should measure 10″ by 12″.

Place the needlepoint right side down on a table. Take the lining fabric and center it over the needlepoint right side up. The lining fabric should extend one inch over the needlepoint on all sides. Along one edge, turn in that extra inch of lining fabric and pin the lining fabric (with the extra inch turned under against the wrong side of the needlepoint) to the needlepoint itself. Keep the edge of the lining straight. Continue the process of pinning and turning one inch of lining under along the other three sides.

After all four sides are pinned together, there should be no wrinkles in the lining. It should lie flat and taut atop the needlepoint. Take the sewing needle and matching thread and stitch the lining and needlepoint together along the edge, taking pains to insert the needle through the canvas threads rather than the woolen yarn. I try to make my stitches catch every other canvas thread when I attach my linings, and I use a double thread rather than a single one for additional strength. The stitches should be tiny and as invisible as you can make them. I recommend the whip stitch rather than a hemming stitch. Eventually all four sides will be stitched together, and you can begin to turn your work into what you envisioned.

BELTS

When estimating the length of canvas needed for a belt, use the waist measurement and add two or three inches to it. A certain amount of the length will be lost when the ends of the belt are stitched over the buckles and when the belt is worn over layers of clothing. It is always possible to shorten the belt after it is made by turning more needlepoint over the ends of the buckles, but it is impossible to lengthen it. Always, in needlepoint, err on the side of generosity.

Once the ends of the needlepoint are stitched over the buckles, the man's belt in this collection is completed. The woman's beaded belt was embellished with a chain of beads at the lower edge. This was done by threading a dozen seed beads onto three strands of silk buttonhole twist (the same thread that was used to attach the beads to the needlepoint canvas) and knotting the thread to the bottom edge of the belt every half-inch. The process of "string-twelve-onto-the-thread, go-half-an-inch, knot, etc." was continued down the length of the belt.

One end of the belt was sewn over two rings covered with beads and silk twist instead of the usual buckle. Because I realized that with this sort of fastening the "wrong" side of the needlepoint would be pulled through the rings to show on the "right" side of the work, I reversed "right" and "wrong" sides of the needlepoint for the final three inches that were to be pulled through the rings. In that way, only the finished sides would be visible.

If the process sounds complicated, all of it can be avoided by the purchase of a two-piece belt buckle similar to that used for the man's belt.

EYEGLASS CASE

Once the lining was stitched into place, the work was folded in half the long way. Since the case is open on one end, two sides of the needlepoint had to be sewn together at the bottom and along the side. I used my tapestry needle and the yarn from the background of the design and pulled it gently through every woolen stitch on both sides of the bottom of the case. When I came to the corner, I turned it and continued stitching the sides together through every woolen basketweave stitch at each edge opposite the fold. When I came to the upper end, I pulled the yarn through the final stitches twice, just for reinforcement, knotted the yarn, and pulled it through the work between the lining and the wrong side of the needlepoint.

BOOKCOVER

Before I started stitching the design, I carefully measured the book I wanted to cover. I knew that needlepoint shrinks slightly when blocked, but under tension it can stretch slightly, too, and I wanted the bookcover to fit exactly. I allowed only one-quarter inch extra all around for the cover because I knew it would be submitted to tension.

After I had the needlepoint lined, I again measured the height of the book and added one-quarter inch to allow for its thickness. I then decided how deep I wanted the "flaps" (or pockets) of the bookcover to be. Since I thought the cover would look best with very deep pockets, I measured almost all the way to the spine of the book. Allowing for a deep hem at the inner edge of the flap, I cut two pieces of additional lining fabric to fit these dimensions. I whip-stitched these extra pieces of lining fabric to the edges of the needlepoint just as I had with the lining itself, finished the sewing, and slipped the finished cover over the book. It fit perfectly.

LINGERIE CASE

To make the lingerie case, I used a procedure similar to that of the bookcover with some differences. Before stitching the lining to the needlepoint, I pinned ribbons to the center of the front and back edges of the case so that stitching the lining would attach the ribbons to the needlepoint and the case could be tied closed. Each of the sides of the case has two deep pockets rather than the single flap or pocket of the bookcover.

I made no provision for closing the pockets of the case, but there is no reason why zippers cannot be inserted into the upper edges of the pockets. Or you might use snaps or buttons to close them. You might forego the ribbons at the edges of the work entirely, put only one or two pockets on one side of the doubled-over needlepoint with a zipper across the top, and make a handbag instead.

EVENING BAG

In a departure from the use made of Persian yarn elsewhere in this collection, the evening bag was made from single strands of DMC Perlé Cotton #5 for a silkier look. The gold thread in the design was a metallic knitting yarn. I used a piece of #18 canvas that measured 11″ by 21″ for a bag approximately 7″ by 6¼″ after folding and stitching.

Because the #18 canvas is not particularly stiff, I interlined it with heavyweight black Pellon for added body before stitching in the lining. After stitching, I folded the needlepoint approximately into thirds (a look at the photograph shows where the last fold was made) and, with a double strand of Perlé Cotton, I stitched up the sides of the bag with a kind of whip stitch. To close it, I added a large snap to the flap. Last, I sewed a yard of thin gold chain to the sides.

PINCUSHION

After sewing the lining to the little needlepoint circle, I cut another circle of lining fabric that had a radius about 1½″ larger than the needlepoint itself. I pinned it to the needlepoint, making a series of small tucks around the circumference so it would fit, whip-stitched it to the needlepoint, and left a 1″ opening so that the polyester stuffing could be inserted. After stuffing, I sewed the opening closed.

The first ribbon was applied "horizontally" across the pincushion, and then came the "vertical" one. The final addition was the ribbon around the circumference of the needlepoint circle. The ribbon is actually two ribbons that have been stitched together, half-inch velvet ribbon with quarter-inch satin ribbon appliquéd to it for a slightly more luxurious look.

KNIFE-EDGED PILLOW

Once the lining is attached to the needlepointed surface of the pillow, use the surface as the pattern to cut out the back of the pillow, allowing an extra inch all around. Next, use the same pattern to cut two pieces of muslin to hold the stuffing for the pillow. The muslin pieces can be stitched on the machine; a small opening should be left on the fourth side for the stuffing. I like my pillows somewhat softer than rock-hard, and I prefer polyester to foam rubber for stuffing. Sew the opening in the muslin closed. Then take the backing for the pillow and whip-stitch it to the needlepoint on three sides to form a kind of pillowcase. If you like, a zipper can be inserted on the fourth side so that the muslin pillow can be removed and both objects cleaned separately. Otherwise, whip-stitch the fourth side closed after inserting the pillow. Because the design from which this pillow was made already contained its own edging, I preferred to use a fringe around the pillow instead of the usual welting. I combined three kinds of fringes: off-white tassels, blue tassels, and gold fringe. The tapes are just basted to the pillow backing, one atop another, and the whole thing is then whip-stitched together.

TABARD

The tabard is a kind of needlepoint sandwich sign with ribbons at the sides to hold it together. It is made from one piece of canvas that originally measured about 16" by 40". Final length and width were determined by my own measurements because I didn't want it too long or extremely wide. The finished garment measures 11½" by 31½". I should add that I am not quite 61" tall, and I'm sure most people would prefer a vest more appropriate for themselves.

The tabard is really two rectangles 11½" wide by 12½" long joined together by straps that are 6¾" long by about 2" wide. There is an 8" by 6¾" rectangular opening in the center of the garment that was left unworked to enable my head to get through. Aside from the difficulty of cutting a hole in the canvas and stitching the canvas threads down properly to make sure they neither show through to the right side of the work nor ravel, the tabard is relatively easy to make and quite warm and comfortable to wear.

UPHOLSTERY

When upholstery needlepoint is removed from the blocking board, your work is usually finished. It is probably best to leave this job to professionals. An amateur stands a good chance of ruining both the needlepoint and the object that is to be upholstered. Let me tell you what I did to upholster the footstool in the photograph and then you can make your own decision.

The footstool was originally tufted, so I had to strip it to bare wood and rearrange its stuffing to make its surface appear smooth. After the stuffing was in place, I stapled muslin over it, pulling the fabric taut as I went around all four sides from centers to corners. Another pair of hands is very helpful here—one pair to pull on the fabric, and the other to operate the staple gun. I put the staples into the edge of the wood frame where the needlepoint would eventually cover them.

Next, I marked the center of each of the four sides so that my canvas would be centered on the stool. I applied the canvas over the muslin, matching centers, turned the excess canvas under, and hammered three upholstery tacks in the centers of each of the four sides. From that point on, I could work from center to corners on each side. Corners were an enormous problem because of the excessive bulk of several layers of canvas and needlework, and I found they had to be cut. I finished the corners off (somewhat unprofessionally, I admit) with a couple of stitches just to make sure that they would lie smooth and flat, the way professionally upholstered work appears.